Introduction

Which units should you revise?

This Workbook has been designed to support you in preparing for the externally assessed units of your course. Remember that you won't necessarily be studying all of the units included here – it will depend on the qualification you are taking.

BTEC Level 3 National Qualification	Externally assessed units
Certificate	1 Investigating Practitioners' Work
Extended Certificate Foundation Diploma	1 Investigating Practitioners' Work 3 Group Performance Workshop
Diploma	1 Investigating Practitioners' Work 3 Group Performance Workshop 5 Individual Performance Commission
Extended Diploma Extended Diploma (D) Extended Diploma (A) Extended Diploma (MT)	1 Investigating Practitioners' Work 3 Group Performance Workshop 5 Individual Performance Commission 7 Employment Opportunities in the Performing Arts

Your Workbook

Each unit in this Workbook contains a revision task, similar to the one you will be set for your actual assessment. Working through these will help you to become familiar with the way in which you will be assessed and to develop the skills you require.

This Workbook will often include one or more useful features that explain or break down longer questions or tasks. Remember that these features won't appear in your actual assessment!

> Grey boxes like this contain **hints and tips** about how to complete a task, interpret a brief, understand a concept or structure your responses.

 This icon will appear next to a partial sample answer to a question or task outcome. You should read the partial answer carefully, then complete it in your own words.

Any text in this font is something that you could write yourself. You might go on to complete it in the space provided.

 This is a revision activity. It won't be one of the outcomes you need to produce in your actual assessment, but it will help you to understand the processes you will need to go through.

 These boxes will show you where you can find more help in Pearson's BTEC National Revision Guide. Visit **www.pearsonschools.co.uk/revise** for more information.

There is often space on the pages of this Workbook for you to write in. However, if you are carrying out research and make ongoing notes, you may want to use separate paper. Similarly, some units will be assessed through submission of digital files, or on screen, rather than on paper. Make sure you read the guidance for each unit that is given to you by Pearson and your teacher.

Contents

A small bit of small print

Pearson publishes Sample Assessment Material and the Specification on its website. This is the official content and this book should be used in conjunction with it. The questions in this book have been written to help you practise the knowledge and skills you will require for your assessment. Remember: the real assessment may not look like this.

REVISE BTEC NATIONAL
Performing Arts

REVISION WORKBOOK

Series Consultant: Harry Smith

Authors: Emma Hindley and Heidi McEntee

A note from the publisher

While the publishers have made every attempt to ensure that advice on the qualification and its assessment is accurate, the official specification and associated assessment guidance materials are the only authoritative source of information and should always be referred to for definitive guidance.

This qualification is reviewed on a regular basis and may be updated in the future. Any such updates that affect the content of this Revision Workbook will be outlined at www.pearsonfe.co.uk/BTECchanges.

For the full range of Pearson revision titles across KS2, KS3, GCSE, Functional Skills, AS/A Level and BTEC visit:
www.pearsonschools.co.uk/revise

 Pearson

Published by Pearson Education Limited, 80 Strand, London, WC2R 0RL.

www.pearsonschoolsandfecolleges.co.uk

Copies of official specifications for all Pearson qualifications may be found on the website: qualifications.pearson.com

Text and illustrations © Pearson Education Limited 2018
Typeset and illustrated by Kamae Design
Produced by Out of House Publishing
Cover illustration by Miriam Sturdee

The rights of Emma Hindley and Heidi McEntee to be identified as authors of this work have been asserted by them in accordance with the Copyright, Designs and Patents Act 1988.

First published 2018

21 20 19 18
10 9 8 7 6 5 4 3 2 1

British Library Cataloguing in Publication Data
A catalogue record for this book is available from the British Library

ISBN 978 1 292 15039 0

Acknowledgements
The authors and publisher would like to thank the following individuals and organisations for their kind permission to reproduce copyright material.
Page 75: © Telegraph Media Group Limited 2016.

Photographs
Getty Images: iStock 40, Chung Sung-Jun 75; **Shutterstock:** SpeedKingz 132
All other images © Pearson Education

Notes from the publisher
Pearson has robust editorial processes, including answer and fact checks, to ensure the accuracy of the content in this publication, and every effort is made to ensure this publication is free of errors. We are, however, only human, and occasionally errors do occur. Pearson is not liable for any misunderstandings that arise as a result of errors in this publication, but it is our priority to ensure that the content is accurate. If you spot an error, please do contact us at resourcescorrections@pearson.com so we can make sure it is corrected.

Websites
Pearson Education Limited is not responsible for the content of any external internet sites. It is essential for tutors to preview each website before using it in class so as to ensure that the URL is still accurate, relevant and appropriate. We suggest that tutors bookmark useful websites and consider enabling students to access them through the school/college intranet.

Unit 1: Investigating Practitioners' Work

Your set task

Unit 1 will be assessed through a task, which will be set by Pearson. You will need to use your understanding of the contextual factors that influence the practitioners' work and creative intentions, and your ability to critically analyse work and make connections to the theme through communication of independent judgements. You will research and analyse the work of performing arts practitioners in response to a given brief.

Your Revision Workbook

This Workbook is designed to **revise skills** that might be needed in your assessed task. The content, outcomes, questions and answers are provided to help you to revise content and ways of applying your skills. Ask your tutor or check the **Pearson website** for the most up-to-date **Sample Assessment Material** and **Mark Scheme** to get an indication of the structure of your assessed task and what this requires of you. When looking at the Sample Assessment Materials, you should pay attention to the example given in relation to the choice of practitioner, whether any activities need to be completed on computer or by hand, and at what points the different elements should be completed during your assessment, as well as whether or not you may bring notes into the assessment. The details of the actual assessed task may change so always make sure you are up to date.

To support your revision, this Workbook contains a revision task to help you revise skills that might be needed in your assessed task.

You will revise your skills in investigating practitioners' work as you:

- read a brief, select practitioners to investigate using primary and secondary research and document your sources in a bibliography (pages 2–9)
- apply critical analysis of practitioners' work by identifying influences on their work, including details of their themes, genre and target audiences and demonstrating how they have influenced others (pages 10–32)
- consider your own response to a brief that demonstrates an in-depth understanding of performance, production and repertoire supported by perceptive examples (pages 33–38).

> **Links** To help you revise skills that might be needed in your Unit 1 set task this Workbook contains a revision task starting on page 2. See the Introduction on page iii for more information on features included to help you revise.

Revision task

In this Workbook you will be provided with a revision task, with accompanying brief and information. This should be similar to the format of the actual set task for your assessment, although the practitioners and theme will be different. This will help you to practise the skills you require in advance of your Unit 1 assessment.

Revision task brief

A performing arts event is being organised. This year, all of the performances will be based on the theme of 'Human Rights'. You have been asked by the organisers to investigate contextual influences and critically analyse the work.

The organisers would like you to explore the theme of 'Human Rights' and justify the inclusion of the work of your two chosen practitioners in relation to the theme. In addition, they would like you to recommend which one of the practitioners you have investigated best demonstrates the theme through their work. The practitioners' work will then headline the festival.

Before you begin the activity, you are required to complete the following preparatory work:

1 Research the theme of 'Human Rights'.

2 Select **two** practitioners. The **first** must be **one** from the following practitioners list:
   • Christopher Bruce
   • Augusto Boal.

3 Select a **second** practitioner of your own choice whose work addresses the theme of 'Human Rights'. A practitioner can be an individual or a company with international recognition and an established reputation and presence.

> **Links** In your actual assessment, you may have more practitioners to choose from, but you should choose one of these for the purposes of this Workbook. See page 3 for more information on these practitioners.

> For the purposes of this Workbook, the other practitioner investigated is Konstantin Stanislavski.

During the investigation of your selected practitioners' work, you will need to:

• research both of your selected practitioners using a range of relevant sources
• select relevant information related to the practitioners' work and the theme
• record information
• collate information
• reference and document your research in the form of a bibliography.

> In your actual assessment, you may not be allowed to refer to notes, or there may be restrictions on the length and type of notes that are allowed. Check with your tutor or look at the most up-to-date Sample Assessment Material on the Pearson website for information.

Choosing a practitioner

This page gives background information to the theme and the two practitioners you have been given for your revision task. You will need to choose one of these practitioners before beginning your work.

Theme: Human rights

Human rights are moral principles or norms that describe certain standards of human behaviour. They are regularly protected as legal rights in municipal and international law. They embrace core principles such as dignity, fairness, equality, respect and autonomy, which apply to everyone. Human rights laws differ from country to country. The UK has signed the European Convention on Human Rights (ECHR), which is an international treaty to protect human rights and fundamental freedoms in Europe.

Performing arts practitioners and influential companies past and present have explored the theme of human rights in their work, and challenged their audiences to think about political and social themes relating to human rights.

Practitioner Number One: Christopher Bruce (1945–)

Christopher Bruce is a leading British choreographer and performer. He was artistic director of Rambert Dance Company until 2002 and choreographed many pieces for ballet companies such as Houston Ballet and English National Ballet. He is often political in his work, and combines ballet with modern dance. He believes that human rights themes have been a strong source of inspiration for him, particularly evident in *Ghost Dances*, *Swansong* and *Cruel Garden*. Such is his interest in human rights that Amnesty International UK and Rambert have collaborated on publicity and the preparation of school resources for *Swansong*, which is based on the interrogation of a prisoner by two prison guards. *'Social and political themes emerge naturally as a reflection of his own concerns, although his aim is always firstly to create a piece of dance, rather than to make a statement.'*

(Source: www.criticaldance.com)

Practitioner Number Two: Augusto Boal (1931–2009)

Augusto Boal was a Brazilian theatre director, writer and politician. He created the Theatre of the Oppressed which is a theatrical form first used in radical popular education movements. In the Theatre of the Oppressed, the audience becomes active, so that rather than being spectators they become 'spect-actors' and explore, show, analyse and transform the reality in which they are living. Boal also developed other acting methods such as 'legislative theatre'. He adapted these methods to social conditions in Brazil, demonstrating a left-wing approach; he was an activist and his teachings were controversial. Boal's techniques use theatre as a means of promoting social and political change.

'Theater of the Oppressed, which Mr. Boal created in the early 1970s and which has become an international theater movement with adherents in more than 40 countries, is politically as well as artistically motivated. Its productions take aim at injustice, especially in communities, often poor or otherwise disenfranchised, that are traditionally voiceless.'

(Source: www.nytimes.com)

Investigation process

The first thing you should do is to think about the areas you will need to cover in your assessment. Set yourself **clear aims** and **objectives**.

Guided

 Complete the table below, jotting down notes relating to the four assessment outcomes. What is your understanding of them? How might you complete the work required for each one? Some of the information has already been completed to get you started.

Knowledge and understanding of contextual factors that influence the practitioners' work and creative intentions	Relationship between contextual factors, creative intentions and themes	Critical analysis of the practitioners' work	Present conclusions and independent judgements via effective investigation
Look at social and political background	Find out how the practitioner described their own contextual influences	Break down the different parts of practitioners' works	Try to add my own opinions
Do some research about the period of history in which my practitioners lived	Watch a play by one of my practitioners to understand what themes they are communicating and how	Explain the effects of the different techniques the practitioners have used	Link my own opinions to things I have discovered during my research

Primary research

Primary research means creating and collecting research yourself. This is an opportunity to think about the primary research you could carry out to help you write your piece of writing.

> ✏️ Work through the questions below to ensure that you are clear on what primary research is and how you can carry this out.

> Guided > 1 Jot down three different ways of conducting primary research, which are relevant to the unit.

Watching a live performance,..

....

> 🔗 **Links** You can find out more about potential primary research sources on page 5 of the Revision Guide.

> Guided > 2 Taking the theme of human rights in relation to your selected practitioners, undertake some primary research. Record it in note form below.

I watched footage of Christopher Bruce's 'Swansong' online. The use of gunshot-style audio

effects and contemporary militaristic costumes supported the idea that Bruce is concerned with

the theme of human rights. ....

....

....

....

....

....

....

....

3 What do you think are the advantages and disadvantages of conducting primary research?

....

....

....

....

....

....

....

> Think about these advantages and disadvantages when writing about your findings in your extended writing.

Secondary research

Secondary research is about collecting information from existing research. This is an opportunity to think about the secondary research you could carry out to help with your assessment.

 Work through the questions below to ensure that you are clear on what secondary research is and how you can carry this out.

Guided

1 Jot down **six** different sources where secondary research can be located.

On the internet, in archives, ...

....

....

Guided

2 Undertake some secondary research based on the theme of human rights in relation to your selected practitioners.

Boal OR Bruce

I did some research on the internet about human rights and Boal. I discovered that Boal used

forum theatre to help the audience to engage in real-life human rights issues, coining the phrase

'spect-actors'. ....

....

....

....

....

....

....

....

Stanislavski

....

....

....

....

....

....

....

....

....

Make sure you keep notes of your sources as you go along. This will save time at the end!

Collating information

As part of the research process, you will need to **collect** and **combine** information from different sources. Prioritise the information that is most relevant to your writing.

> **1** To practise your skills in selecting and rejecting information, select the three most significant pieces of information related to your two chosen practitioners. Put a tick against the information that you wish to select, and a cross against your rejections.
>
> **Augusto Boal**
>
> **A** ☐ Died of respiratory failure.
>
> **B** ☐ Most respected Brazilian theatre practitioner abroad.
>
> **C** ☐ Created 'Theatre of the Oppressed' – originally used in radical popular education movements.
>
> **D** ☐ Often adapted his methods to social conditions in Brazil.
>
> **E** ☐ Wanted his audiences to express themselves – socially liberating.
>
> **OR**
>
> **Christopher Bruce**
>
> **A** ☐ One of the UK's leading choreographers.
>
> **B** ☐ Artistic director of Rambert Dance Company and choreographed for several ballet companies.
>
> **C** ☐ Visiting professor at Exeter University.
>
> **D** ☐ Grew up in Scarborough.
>
> **E** ☐ Uses social themes as a source of inspiration.
>
> **Konstantin Stanislavski**
>
> **A** ☐ Grew up in one of the richest families in Russia.
>
> **B** ☐ His interests included the circus.
>
> **C** ☐ Was influenced by Marxism.
>
> **D** ☐ Developed method acting – acting from the inside out.
>
> **E** ☐ Was an advocate of equal opportunities for every human being.

Guided ▷ **2** Combine the information from question 1 with any other relevant information which you jotted down from your primary and secondary research on previous pages. Create a spider diagram for each of your two practitioners. Ensure that all of the information has been collated effectively so that there is no overlap. Also ensure that there is no irrelevant information included.

> If necessary, use a separate piece of paper to collate all your information and remove irrelevant information before finally completing these spider diagrams.

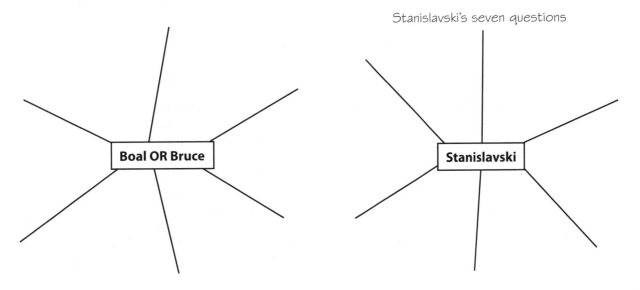

Stanislavski's seven questions

Boal OR Bruce

Stanislavski

Documenting research sources

Your bibliography to your assessment will need to be **logical** and **consistent**. Remember it is an assessed element, so you need to invest time into it. This is an opportunity to think about what your bibliography should contain and how you will need to present it.

 Work through the questions on this page to practice the skills you need to reference effectively.

Guided 1 Write down what information is required when you are referencing a book. One example has already been provided.

Author's name

....

....

....

Guided 2 Write down what information is required when you are referencing a website. One example has already been provided.

Title of website

....

....

....

3 Do you need to use quotation marks if you are quoting directly from a source?

....

4 If you have performed background reading but have not cited/quoted directly from a source, do you still need to reference this in the bibliography?

....

5 What are footnotes, and how do you use them?

....

....

....

....

6 How can you keep your bibliography organised? Write down **three** ideas.

....

....

....

Links You can learn more about citation and referencing on page 11 of the Revision Guide.

Presentation of findings: referencing, citation and bibliography

Work through the questions on this page to practise the skills needed to provide an organised bibliography.

1 What is the difference between citing and quoting from a source?

....

....

2 Do you need to provide a page number if you have quoted/cited from a book or journal?

....

3 Do you need to provide a paragraph number if you are quoting from a website?

....

Guided 4 Read this bibliography extract:

> http://method.vtheatre.net/stanislavsky.html
>
> Para 2
>
> Stanislavksi, C, An Actor Prepares, Bloomsbury Revelations, 2013, Bloomsbury Academic
>
> Boal, A, Theatre of the Oppressed (Get Political), 2008, Pluto Press
>
> https://en.wikipedia.org/wiki/Christopher_Bruce
>
> https://en.wikipedia.org/wiki/Augusto_Boal

Name several ways in which the information could be improved, and state what information is missing. One example has already been provided.

Dates when web pages were accessed should be included for all websites.

....

....

....

....

....

....

Links See page 11 of the Revision Guide to revise referencing, citation and bibliography.

Historical and cultural contextual factors

Your writing will be assessed on your knowledge and understanding of the contextual factors that influence your chosen practitioners' work. Contextual factors are historical, cultural, economic, political, technological, social, geographical and physical events and ideas.

> ✏️ Use the following four pages to consider different types of contextual factors and how they might relate to your practitioners' work.

Guided > **1** What are historical factors?

Historical factors are factors that relate to key historical events and epoch, such as ....

....

2 What are cultural factors?

....

....

Guided > **3** Complete the following information in relation to one of your selected practitioners. Try to relate your contextual factor(s) to the theme (human rights) as far as possible.

.... was influenced by ....

The effect of this on his work is ....

....

....

Guided > **4** Complete the spider diagram below in relation to Konstantin Stanislavski.

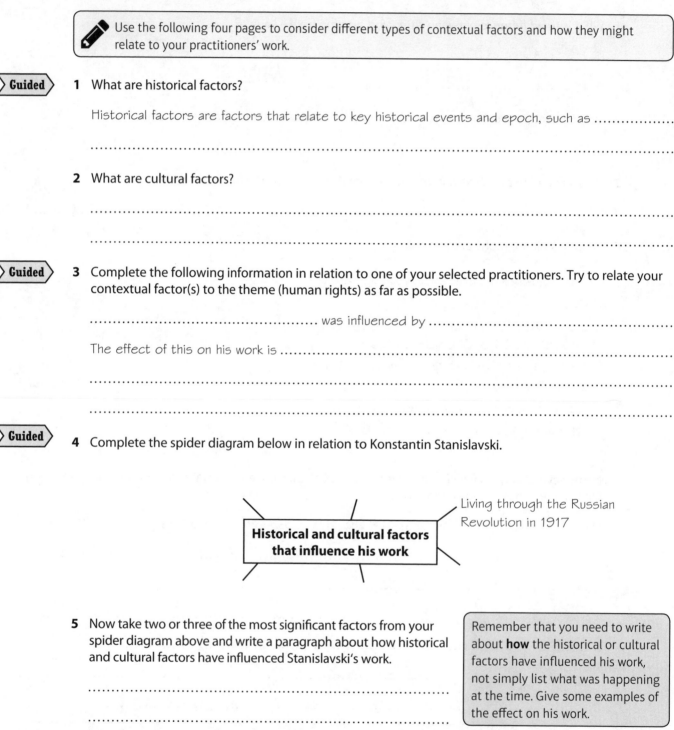

Living through the Russian Revolution in 1917

Historical and cultural factors that influence his work

5 Now take two or three of the most significant factors from your spider diagram above and write a paragraph about how historical and cultural factors have influenced Stanislavski's work.

Remember that you need to write about **how** the historical or cultural factors have influenced his work, not simply list what was happening at the time. Give some examples of the effect on his work.

....

....

....

....

> 🔗 **Links** For more information on how historical and cultural factors can influence a practitioner's work, see page 13 of the Revision Guide

Economic and political contextual factors and practitioners' work

Guided **1** What are economic factors?

Economic factors are related to funding conditions and ....

....

Guided **2** What are political factors?

Political factors are related to legislation, ...

....

Guided **3** Complete the table below, adding information about both of your selected practitioners which relates to economic and political factors. Remember you also need to explain the effect this had on their work. One example has already been provided.

Boal OR Bruce	Stanislavski
	He was under permanent surveillance, because his Moscow Art Theatre was frequently attended by dictators such as Joseph Stalin. This meant that…

Links For more information on how economic and political factors can influence a practitioner's work, see page 14 of the Revision Guide.

Technical and social contextual factors

Guided **1** What are technical factors?

Technical factors are related to the latest developments in technology as well as ....

....

Guided **2** What are social factors?

Social factors are factors that affect lifestyle, such as ....

....

Guided **3** Complete the following information in relation to one of your selected practitioners. Try to relate it to the theme if you can.

.... was influenced by ....

The effect of this on his work is ....

....

....

....

4 Complete the spider diagram below in relation to Boal OR Bruce.

Technical and social factors that influence their work

5 Now take the key points from your spider diagram above and write a paragraph about how technical and social factors have influenced Boal OR Bruce.

Remember that you need to write about **how** the technical or social factors have influenced their work, not simply list the factors. Give some examples of how you see the influence on their work.

....

....

....

....

....

....

....

🔗 **Links** For more information on how technical and social factors can influence a practitioner's work, see page 15 of the Revision Guide

Geographical and physical contextual factors

Guided **1** What are geographical factors?

Geographical factors are ....

Guided **2** What are physical factors?

Physical factors are related to the physical characteristics of ....

....

Guided **3** Complete the table below, adding information about both of your selected practitioners which relates to geographical and physical factors. Remember to also think about the effect of these factors on his work. One example has already been provided.

Boal OR Bruce	Stanislavski
Boal was influenced by being raised in Brazil. We can see this affecting his work in…	

Influences

In your writing, it's important to think about how other people may have influenced the work of your chosen practitioners.

> ✎ Use the questions below to help you consider how you might discuss this in your response.

1 What does it mean if a practitioner is 'influenced' by someone?

....

....

2 Who might practitioners be influenced by? Think of **four** examples.

....

....

3 For **one** of your selected practitioners, complete the spider diagram below.

People who have influenced their work

4 For your **other** selected practitioner, write a list of who they have been influenced by.

....

....

....

Guided **5** For each of the practitioners, think about **how** they were influenced. Did it affect the material they were creating? Some of their influences may be related to the theme of human rights. Complete the paragraph below.

Boal/Bruce was influenced by .... in terms of how ....

....

....

....

Stanislavski was influenced by .... regarding ....

....

....

....

Themes

Thinking about the themes of your chosen practitioners' work, and how those themes are communicated to the audience, is an important part of considering their creative intention.

 Answer the questions below to help you formulate insightful connections between the creative intentions of practitioners' work and the theme, making sure you use examples.

1 Think about how each of the following practitioners explored the theme of 'human rights' in their work. Make a list below.

Boal OR Bruce

....

....

....

....

Stanislavski

....

....

....

....

Guided 2 For each practitioner, take the theme of human rights and think about how it was communicated. Consider what techniques and methods each of the practitioners used.

Boal/Bruce communicated the theme of .... by ....

....

....

....

....

Stanislavski communicated the theme of .... by ....

....

....

....

....

3 Themes often recur through history, but what brings them alive is the practitioner's ability to present them in new and refreshing ways. How did your selected practitioners achieve this? How were their techniques and methods different from the people who influenced them? Write some notes below.

....

....

....

....

....

....

Links For more information about considering themes behind a practitioner's work, see page 18 of the Revision Guide.

Intentions, genre and target audiences

✎ Answer the questions below to consider how the genres of your chosen practitioners' work, and the audience they were targeting, affect their creative intention.

1 What does the word genre mean?

....

> *Genre* is a French word which you can look up.

Guided ⟩ **2** Complete the paragraph below about genre in relation to your two selected practitioners.

The genre best used to describe the work of Boal/Bruce is ....

....

His work is typical/not typical of the genre because ....

....

....

The genre best used to describe the work of Stanislavski is ....

His work is typical/not typical of the genre because ....

....

....

3 What is a target audience?

....

Guided ⟩ **4** Complete the sentences below.

The target audience for Boal/Bruce's work is ....

....

The target audience for Stanislavski's work is ....

> Remember there may be more than one target audience, but think about the **key** group targeted by each practitioner

....

....

5 Write a paragraph about one practitioner's creative intention of using their chosen genre on the specific target audience. Think about how this audience would react to some of the features of the genre, and why.

....

....

....

....

 Links To revise this area, see page 19 of the Revision Guide.

Influencing other people

Not only will your practitioners have been influenced by a number of factors, but they will in turn have influenced others through their work. Thinking about who they have influenced and how will help you critically analyse your chosen practitioners' work.

 Answer the questions below to identify how your chosen practitioners have influenced others.

1 Complete the table below, filling out **who** your selected practitioners influenced and **how**.

	Who	How
Boal OR Bruce		
Stanislavski		

2 Do the selected practitioners continue to have an impact on the work of practitioners today? Try to provide examples if possible.

....

....

....

....

....

....

Links To revise how practitioners influence others, see page 20 of the Revision Guide.

Collaborations

Collaborating with other people can influence a practitioner's work and creative intentions.

> ✏️ Work through the questions below to investigate how collaboration is linked to creative intentions.

1 What is a collaboration?

....

....

2 Who might practitioners collaborate with?

....

....

Guided ⟩ **3** Complete a spider diagram for each of your practitioners, stating who they collaborated with.

Collaborations: Boal OR Bruce	**Collaborations: Stanislavski**

Collaborated with the writers Tolstoy and Chekhov

4 Write a paragraph about how your practitioners' collaborations impacted on the material they created and the intentions they communicated.

....

....

....

....

....

....

....

....

....

....

> Remember to keep documenting the sources in which you find information as you go along. You could record all the information in a notebook or an electronic file, or on separate filing cards for each source.

> 🔗 **Links** To revise collaborations, see page 21 in the Revision Guide.

Public and critical responses

 Think about the public and critical responses to your practitioners' work. Answer the questions below to help develop your critical analysis skills.

Remember that public and critical responses can vary greatly. Try to consider a range of responses in order to gain a more balanced picture.

1 What is meant by public and critical responses to a practitioner's work? Why are they significant?

....

....

....

....

2 How might public and critical responses affect practitioners?

....

....

....

....

Guided 3 Complete the paragraph below in relation to public and critical responses to your selected practitioners' work.

Public and critical responses to Boal/Bruce's work include ....

....

....

....

This affected his work by ....

....

....

Public and critical responses to Stanislavski's work include ....

....

....

....

This affected his work by ....

....

....

....

Performance styles: repertoire

The performance styles and methods that characterise a practitioner's work help to communicate meaning.

> ✏ Answer the questions over the following page, they will help you to critically analyse your chosen practitioners' work and creative intentions. On this page you will explore repertoire.

1 What is repertoire?

....

2 Why is repertoire significant?

....

....

Guided **3** Complete the spider diagram below to describe what repertoire can consist of.

Repertoire

Score

Guided **4** Think about repertoire in relation to one of your selected practitioners. Complete the paragraph below.

Repertoire in relation to the practitioner is significant because ....

....

....

Repertoire is used by the practitioner to communicate meaning by ....

....

....

The style/genre of the repertoire is ....

....

although some work is not so typical of the genre, such as ....

....

....

5 In relation to your other selected practitioner, write down a list of key words regarding repertoire and how it communicates meaning.

....

....

....

> 🔗 **Links** To revise performance styles and methods see pages 27–31 of the Revision Guide.

Performance styles: performance

✏️ Answer the questions on this page to explore how practitioners use the elements of performance to communicate meaning.

Look at this spider diagram. Jot down key points relating to each element, and how each of your selected practitioners uses them to communicate meaning.

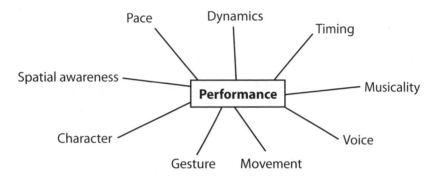

Boal OR Bruce

Pace ....

Dynamics ....

Timing ....

Musicality ....

Voice ....

Movement ....

Gesture ....

Character ....

Spatial awareness ....

Stanislavski

Pace ....

Dynamics ....

Timing ....

Musicality ....

Voice ....

Movement ....

Gesture ....

Character ....

Spatial awareness ....

Performance styles: relationships

> ✏ Answer the questions on this page to explore how different relationships affect practitioners' work.

Guided 1 Make a list of different relationships that may affect practitioners' work. Provide at least **six** examples.

Performer to audience ....

....

....

Guided 2 Now write **one** sentence about **each** of the different relationships, stating what it means.

Performer to audience could mean the audience being involved in the performance ....

....

....

....

....

....

Guided 3 Complete the paragraph below in relation to your selected practitioners.

Relationships between musical accompaniment and dance are used in the work of Bruce; for

example, in 'Swansong' he ....

....

Other relationships that are used in his work are ....

....

....

These are significant because they communicate ....

....

Stanislavski wanted his performer/audience relationship to be close, drawing the audience in

through ....

....

Other relationships that are used in his work are ....

....

....

These are significant because they communicate ....

....

....

Performance styles: production, design and technical

 Work through the questions below to explore how production, design and technical aspects of a performance affect practitioners' work.

1 Look at the spider diagram below. Select **three** elements to focus on for each of your selected practitioners. Jot them down below.

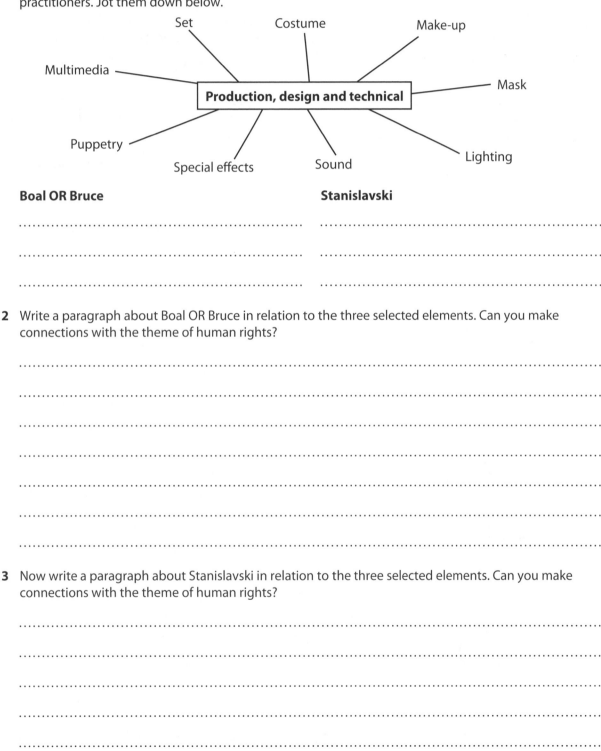

Set   Costume   Make-up

Multimedia

Production, design and technical

Mask

Puppetry

Special effects   Sound

Lighting

Boal OR Bruce   **Stanislavski**

....

....

....

2 Write a paragraph about Boal OR Bruce in relation to the three selected elements. Can you make connections with the theme of human rights?

....

....

....

....

....

....

....

3 Now write a paragraph about Stanislavski in relation to the three selected elements. Can you make connections with the theme of human rights?

....

....

....

....

....

....

....

....

Summarise key information

You will need to be able to summarise key information to support the independent judgements that you make. Practise those skills on this page.

1 Why is it important only to use information that is valid?

....

....

When you are analysing, remember that you are not only focusing on the practitioners. You will also need to analyse a piece of repertoire/extract.

Guided **2** Select a piece of repertoire by one of your chosen practitioners. Break it down into parts so that you are considering the following elements: repertoire, performance, relationships, and production, design and technical. Complete the table below.

	Boal	**Bruce**	**Stanislavski**
Piece	Theatre of the Oppressed	Swansong	The Three Sisters
Repertoire			
Performance			He used a combination of performance elements to communicate a realistic expression of emotion, wanting the performers to fully immerse themselves in...
Relationships			
Production, design and technical		Props, set, costume, lighting and sound all contribute significantly. He uses the chair to...	

Remember to: consider alternative viewpoints; refer to contextual influences; make connections/links between theme(s), creative intentions and influences in the material selected; and consider genre and style.

Analyse and explore

In order to critically analyse practitioners' work, you will need to use the following skills: analysis and exploration. Answer the questions below to practise these skills.

1 'Analyse' means ....

2 'Explore' means ....

Guided

3 Taking one of your selected practitioners, try to analyse the contextual factors that influenced their work. Start off by stating a contextual factor and then providing an example of the effect on their work. Finally, provide an explanation of what this shows about the practitioner's creative intention. One example has been provided.

Contextual factor	Influence on practitioner	Explanation
Chile was going through a violent coup (political factor) and Bruce met the widow of a murdered Chilean musician	This meeting inspired him to choreograph Ghost Dances	He wanted to highlight the plight of innocent South Americans. ....
....	....	....
....	....	....
....	....	....

You could expand on the information above by transferring the information into a paragraph or two of extended writing.

4 You need to **explore** and understand alternative viewpoints. Focusing on one work of Boal, Bruce or Stanislavski write down a list of audience responses and critics' opinions using key words only.

....

....

....

....

5 Now write a paragraph exploring the different interpretations of the practitioner's work, possible reasons for these and whether you feel they are justified, with evidence.

....

....

....

....

....

....

....

Interpreting and prioritising information

 To develop your critical analysis skills, you will also need to be able to interpret and prioritise information. Answer the questions below to practise these skills.

1 'Interpret' means ....

2 'Prioritise' means ....

3 Focusing on one of your selected practitioners, make a list of facts about their work. You should write a list of bullet points rather than complete sentences.

....

....

....

....

....

4 Now write down a number against each fact, in order of priority. If you think some are of equal importance, you can use a number more than once.

5 Take the facts above and write a paragraph where you **interpret** the information. For example, what is the significance of the information? How has this impacted on the practitioner's work? How does it relate to the theme?

....

....

....

....

....

....

....

....

....

....

Remember that you can provide any interpretation you want as long as you back it up with examples to justify your decision(s).

Evaluating and making independent judgements

 You need to be able to evaluate information and make independent judgements when writing about your two practitioners. Answer the questions below to practise these skills.

1 'Evaluate' means ....

2 'Make independent judgements' means ....

3 Select one of your practitioners. Make a list of what you believe to be strengths and weaknesses in relation to their work. Are any examples related to the theme of human rights?

Strengths	Weaknesses
....	....
....	....
....	....
....	....
....	....

4 Thinking about the same practitioner you used for question 3, create a spider diagram of the evidence for your statements in question 3.

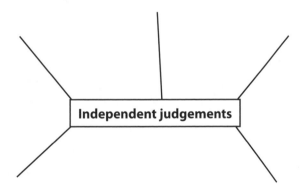

Independent judgements

You could expand on the information above by writing a paragraph of extended writing, evaluating the practitioner's work. Remember, you need to cover both strengths and weaknesses, and explain why you think the point is a strength or weakness, giving examples from their work. You will also need to come to a conclusion when you evaluate effectively (see pages 28–29 for more advice on conclusion).

Conclusions, links and further investigation 1

Answer the questions on this page to practise the skills of drawing conclusions, establishing links and making comparisons with the work of other performing arts practitioners. You can also explore opportunities for further investigation into your practitioners' work.

1 Complete the spider diagram with conclusions you have drawn about one of your selected practitioners.

Your conclusions will depend on the practitioner. For Boal, for example, you could include how he was influenced by his upbringing in Brazil, while Bruce was influenced by his ballet training. However, you might find that there are links and similarities in their aims and the messages they wished to communicate to their audiences.

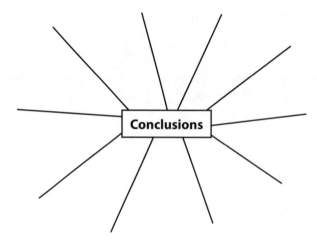

2 Make a list of similarities/links between the work of one of your practitioners and the work of other practitioners.

....

....

....

....

....

....

Conclusions, links and further investigation 2

1 Now expand on the information on page 28 by writing a paragraph about the similarities, exploring **how** and **why** they are connected.

....

....

....

....

....

....

....

....

....

....

....

....

....

2 Why might it be useful to highlight how opportunities for further investigation could be explored?

....

....

....

....

....

....

....

....

....

....

....

....

Presentation of findings: format, structure and tone

 Answer the questions on this page to practise the skills needed to present your findings effectively, using an appropriate format, structure and tone in your writing.

 Links To revise presentation of your findings, see pages 35 and 36 of the Revision Guide.

Guided 1 Write a short plan for your presentation. You should include headings for each of the different sections, and briefly describe what will be in each one.

Introduction

Influences for practitioner 1 ....

....

....

....

....

....

....

....

....

....

....

....

Guided 2 The tone of your written work will need to be formal rather than conversational. Jot down some sentence starters that you could use in your written work. Some examples have already been provided.

According to research sources ....

I have come to the conclusion that ....

....

....

....

....

....

Read other pieces of formal writing, for example when carrying out your secondary research, to understand how to structure your writing and use a formal tone.

Presentation of findings: language and subject-specific terminology

Use the activities below to practise the skills needed to present your findings using appropriate language and terminology that is relevant to the subject. Be clear and confident!

1 Look at the phrases below. Select the **three** that are the most appropriate for use in your extended writing.

☐ I believe that Boal's use of political themes is effective because …

☐ I think Boal is good because …

☐ Christopher Bruce's dances are great for the following reasons …

☐ Bruce's work is highly successful due to several factors …

☐ Stanislavski was original in his use of …

☐ Stanislavski was really different in what he did …

> **Guided**

2 Complete this table with terminology that is specific to each performing arts sector. Some examples have already been provided.

Dance	Acting	Musical theatre
Choreography	Dialogue	Pitch

3 Write a paragraph about one of your selected practitioners in relation to the theme of human rights. Make sure that you use appropriate language as well as subject-specific terminology.

....

....

....

....

....

....

....

....

....

Proofread your work carefully once you have completed it. Check your grammar as well as spelling. Make sure your sentences aren't too long and that you use a separate paragraph for each key point you cover.

Presenting structured arguments

> 🖊 Complete the activities below to ensure that your arguments are logically structured.

1   What do you need to remember when presenting structured arguments, conclusions and judgements? Provide at least three suggestions.

....

....

....

....

2   How could the following extract of writing be improved in terms of structure, conclusions and judgements?

> Swansong is about prison guards and their treatment of a prisoner; in Cruel Garden the piece relates to fascism and Ghost Dances is about victims of political oppression in South America. This shows that Bruce was a leading British choreographer. He was encouraged to learn how to dance by his father.

....

....

....

....

....

Guided 3   It is important to provide examples in your writing in order to back up your decisions. Focusing on the work of your selected practitioners, complete the following sentences, using examples to back up the statements.

Stanislavski's methods were influenced by previous practitioners ....

....

Bruce choreographed work for many ballet companies ....

....

Boal developed several theatre techniques ....

....

> Remember to use phrases like 'such as', 'for example' or 'for instance' when providing examples.

Your own response

This section of the Workbook provides you with the opportunity to practise writing a response to the revision task on page 2.

> 🖉 Look back at page 2 now to remind yourself of the task. Use the space on this page to make brief notes on your background research and to compile your bibliography.

....

....

....

....

....

....

....

....

....

Bibliography

> Don't forget to reference all of the information you have used throughout your investigation. Use the sections below to organise your information.

Books

....

....

....

....

Websites

....

....

....

....

Other (digital archives, journals)

....

....

....

....

You are now ready to complete your writing in response to the revision task on page 2. The activity boxes below will help you to think about how you might structure your writing.

 Next you could write about how you think **political factors** have influenced the work of Boal OR Bruce and Stanislavski and their communication of the theme of human rights.

Make sure that you include:
- reference to specific relevant political factors
- reference to specific relevant parts of each practitioners' work influenced by those political factors, using references to the sources you listed in the bibliography
- connections to the theme of human rights.

First you could write about how you think specific contextual factors have influenced the work of Boal OR Bruce and Stanislavski and their communication of the theme. For responding to the revision task, you might want to focus on **political** factors.

....
....
....
....
....
....
....
....
....
....
....
....
....
....
....
....
....
....
....
....
....
....

Over the next two pages you could focus on your critical analysis of your practitioners in relation to the theme of human rights.

Try and highlight both the similarities and differences between the practitioners' use of the elements to communicate the theme.

In this critical analysis, make sure that you:
- reference at least one specific scene or moment for each practitioner, making reference, if applicable, to your research sources listed in the bibliography
- make connections to the theme.

Some of the elements you could discuss include character and dynamics, as well as the use of different production techniques such as lighting and sound.

....
....
....
....
....
....
....
....
....
....
....
....
....
....
....
....
....
....
....
....
....
....

Next you may want to write about specific pieces of repertoire for each practitioner. Choose pieces you are familiar with and which you can use to talk about the theme of human rights to justify the practitioner's inclusion in the performing arts event.

Finally you will need to compose a conclusion. You may like to use the work you did on pages 28 and 29 to help you. Make sure that you include a recommendation for which practitioners' work would be most suitable for the event.

....

....

....

....

....

....

....

....

....

....

....

....

....

Remember to always use clear examples to support your findings, judgements and conclusions.

....

....

....

....

....

....

....

....

....

....

....

....

....

....

....

Unit 3: Group Performance Workshop

Your set task

Unit 3 will be assessed through a task, which will be set by Pearson. You will need to use your understanding of how to interpret and respond to a stimulus, plan, develop and realise creative ideas within a group, and review and reflect on your performance. You will complete a set task that requires you to respond within a group to a stimulus to create and present a group performance, evaluating the different stages of the work.

Your Revision Workbook

This Workbook is designed to **revise skills** that might be needed in your assessed task. The content, outcomes, questions and answers are provided to help you to revise content and ways of applying your skills. Ask your tutor or check the **Pearson website** for the most up-to-date **Sample Assessment Material** and **Mark Scheme** to get an indication of the structure of your assessed task and what this requires of you. When looking at the Sample Assessment Materials, you should pay attention to the details of the target audience for the performance work and time constraints, such as length of performance, number of pieces and available resources as well as how to submit your work. The details of the actual assessed task may change so always make sure you are up to date.

To support your revision, this Workbook contains a revision task to help you revise skills that might be needed in your assessed task.

You will revise your skills in responding to a stimulus and group performance set task as you:

- read, interpret and respond to a set task and selected stimulus, performing research, planning and creatively exploring ideas (pages 40–49)
- develop evaluative skills in relation to the different stages of the creative and performance process (pages 50–59)
- consider how to complete a written response to a set task and selected stimulus, evaluating the effectiveness of each stage of development as well as the final performance (pages 60–72).

Links To help you revise skills that might be needed in your Unit 3 set task, this Workbook contains a revision task starting on page 40. See the Introduction on page iii for more information on features included to help you revise.

Revision task

To support your revision, this Workbook contains a revision task to help you revise the skills that might be needed in your assessed task. You are first guided through how to approach the task with activities; you can then use either the revision task or your own selection of work to work through the steps required more independently.

Although you are given a revision task below that includes a performance piece and digital process log, the Workbook will only require you to focus on the planning aspects and skills associated with the tasks involved. You are NOT expected to undertake a full group performance and associated tasks as part of the Workbook.

Revision task brief

You have been asked to work as part of a small performance company of 3–7 performers to create an original piece of work that you will present as an informal performance to an invited audience.

You are required to use the stimulus below as a basis for developing the piece.

The performance piece needs to be between 10 and 20 minutes long.

The audience will want to see an original piece created in response to the stimulus. Your performance company will need to work together creatively, drawing on all of your strengths to create an imaginative piece of work.

Throughout the task you are required to complete a digital process log.

You must demonstrate your personal contributions to artistic decisions made within the group context in response to:

- planning and interpretation of the stimulus
- development and realisation of creative ideas
- review and reflection of the workshop performance.

The digital process log will capture your contribution to the development and rehearsal process. The log may include embedded digital photographs, video and audio files.

Remember that the performance is only a 'work in progress'. Production elements such as sound or costume may still be undecided or unfinished. You may use music, sound effects, props, costumes and basic staging as suited to a workshop presentation and to give an impression of the creative intention of the work.

Revision task information

Below is the stimulus you should use to create and develop your performance ideas for the purposes of this Workbook.

Stimulus: Poverty

The details of your actual assessed task may change so always make sure you are up to date. Ask your tutor or check the Pearson website for the most up-to-date Sample Assessment Material.

Planning and interpretation of stimulus

To plan and develop a group performance you will need to spend time interpreting the stimulus and planning how to explore this as a group.

 Work through the activities below to practise the skills needed to do this.

Guided **1** Taking the stimulus on page 40, jot down **ten** initial responses to the theme of 'poverty'. Stick to single words or short phrases. Two examples have been provided.

Hunger, homelessness ....

....

....

> You can write down your initial responses to the stimulus you are given in order to effectively write about this when you complete your digital log.

2 Now organise your brainstorm by selecting just six words/phrases you think will work best in terms of exploring the theme when developing your performance, and discarding others. Complete the spider diagram below.

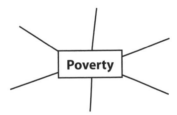

Poverty

3 Taking your six points, think of a suitable starting point for exploring each concept. This may be an idea to research, or more practical methods such as improvisation or hot-seating. Complete the boxes below.

Starting point 1	Starting point 2

Starting point 3	Starting point 4

Starting point 5	Starting point 6

 Links See pages 51–52 of the Revision Guide for more guidance on primary and secondary research.

Research

Research is an essential part of developing a new performance.

 Use the activity below to guide you through undertaking research in response to the revision task on page 40. You should spend no more than 30 minutes on this activity.

Guided 1 Taking the theme of 'poverty', undertake some research. If it is possible, try to undertake both primary and secondary research. Record your research in note form below.

Interesting fact that I found: 'The number of people sleeping rough in London has risen from 3,673 in 2009/2010 to more than 7,500 (in 2015).'

(Source: http://www.independent.co.uk/news/uk/politics/david-cameron-vows-crackdown-on-poverty-on-same-day-as-figures-reveal-homelessness-has-doubled-under-a6792916.html. *The Independent*, headline, last accessed 25 July 2017.)

> Remember to acknowledge all of your sources as you work. Write down websites and relevant publishing details from books/journals. Don't pass off work as your own if you have taken it from another source; this counts as plagiarism and will result in you being penalised.

....

....

....

....

....

....

....

....

....

....

....

....

....

....

> When you are recording your research, try to select only information that 'stands out' as being interesting and relevant. This could be a statistic, a true story, an overview of the issue, an image, a quotation or part of an interview. Your research will probably be a combination of these. Try not to rely on just one source of information; extend your search to gather information from different sources, which can then be collated.

 Links See pages 51–52 of the Revision Guide for more guidance on primary and secondary research.

Form and style of performance

When planning and developing a group performance, you will need to consider what form and style the performance will take.

 Use the questions below to consider this in relation to the revision task on page 40.

1 What is your performance pathway? (Dance, acting or musical theatre)

....

Guided **2** Taking the theme of 'poverty' and your performance pathway, consider what form(s) or style(s) of performance might be effective, and why. One partial example has been provided.

We are going to use contemporary dance to communicate our message on the theme of poverty. We will create a narrative dance, perhaps using the ABA ternary choreographic structure. In the first section we will aim to communicate different ways in which poverty affects people.

....

....

....

....

....

....

....

....

....

....

....

3 Can you envisage any difficulties in communicating this theme within your chosen performance pathway? Why? Suggest how any difficulties could be overcome.

....

....

....

....

....

....

Links To revise different types of form and style of performance, see page 49 of the Revision Guide.

Artistic intention and target audience

When planning your group performance, you must ensure you take account of who the target audience is and how you will communicate your artistic aims and intentions.

> 🖉 Use the activities below to describe your artistic intentions.

1 What do you think might be your artistic intention?

> You can give write down a few ideas at this stage, giving some reasons connected with the theme.

....

....

....

....

Guided **2** How could you communicate your artistic intention? Give a total of **six** examples.

Dialogue: for example ....

....

....

....

....

....

3 Who will be your target audience?

> You may not know who your actual audience will be at this stage, but you should have a target audience in mind, some of whom will be able to attend.

....

....

....

....

Guided **4** Which features of your target audience do you need to consider and, how might this affect your performance? Give at least **six** examples.

The age range of our audience will be .... so we will need to consider ....

....

....

....

....

....

....

....

Creative/staging possibilities

When planning a group performance, you must take into account the practical performance skills you and your group can apply to the performance piece.

> Work through the activities on this page to assess your own skills in relation to the revision task on page 40.

1 Taking the theme of 'poverty', consider your creative and staging possibilities. Would the performance lend itself to being site-specific, or would a more traditional theatre space be suitable? Jot down a few notes below.

....

....

....

....

....

Guided 2 Imagine that you are taking a performance about 'child poverty' to a junior school to help communicate the issues surrounding this theme. The performance will be staged in the school hall. Consider the skills you possess that may enhance the performance. List five strengths and five weaknesses of your own performance skills that are relevant to your particular performance pathway.

1 Strength – my good voice projection helps to deliver clear dialogue in the school hall

1 Weakness – I don't always use the available performance space effectively

....

....

....

....

....

Guided 3 How can you improve your skills for each weakness listed? Use specific examples.

1 To use space better, I could move to another area of the school hall each time my character describes having to move location when sleeping rough on the street.

....

....

....

....

....

....

....

....

Development of creative ideas

Once you have completed the initial planning stages, it is time to develop your ideas further. You can do this through improvisation.

 The activities on this page will help you consider improvisation in relation to the revision task on page 40.

Guided   **1**   What do you need to consider when improvising? Complete the spider diagram below with suggestions.

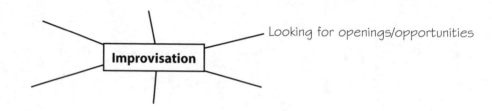

Improvisation

Looking for openings/opportunities

2   Make a list of **five** different ways that you could explore the theme of poverty as part of a group. Think about specific exercises or tasks that your tutor may have set you previously.

....

....

....

....

....

Guided   **3**   Write down **five** ways of capturing the experimentation process.

Making notes ....

....

....

....

....

....

4   Give **two** examples of known practitioners whose techniques and methods you could use when experimenting in response to the theme of poverty for this revision task.

....

....

....

....

 Links   You can revise ways that improvisation and experimentation can be used to respond to a stimulus on pages 55 and 56 of the Revision Guide.

Technical elements

When you are developing your creative ideas, you will need to think about how technical elements will influence your performance.

 Think about some of your recent performances and answer the questions below to explore this further.

1 Think about some recent material you have performed in class. How could it have been improved by the use of costumes, props and basic staging? What would these particular elements have added to the performance? Complete the table below.

Although your performance is a 'work in progress' and will use natural/general lighting, you can still use costume, props and basic staging to enhance your performance.

Costume	Props	Basic staging

Music and sound effects can also play an important part in your performance. If you are following the dance/musical theatre pathway, music will probably be a vital component of your performance. For the acting pathway, music and sound effects may be added in order to create an atmosphere/mood, establish a setting/character or develop the plot further.

2 Think back to when you last performed **on stage**. What did you have to consider that is different from performing in a classroom or studio?

....

....

....

....

....

....

....

Structure

When developing your creative ideas, you will need to ensure in the planning stages that your material has a clear structure.

> ✎ Use the questions below to consider what this could mean in the context of the revision task on page 40.

1 Look back at your list of six key initial responses to the theme of 'poverty' on page 41. How could these key words form the basis of a motif?

....

....

....

....

....

....

....

2 Consider how you could develop the motif by using choreographic devices and structure(s).

....

....

....

....

....

....

....

....

3 Explain why your chosen structure and/or devices would be effective in communicating your theme. Have you used them before, and was this successful?

....

....

....

....

....

....

....

> 🔗 **Links** To revise structure in different performance genres, see page 58 of the Revision Guide.

Developing and shaping material

Developing a performance is a continuous process which means you will need to review and discuss your decisions, and repeatedly make changes until you and your group are happy.

 Answer the questions below to ensure that you are clear about how this works.

1 Explain why the following elements are a crucial part of the creative process.

> You should include examples from your own experience to illustrate the benefits of each element. How will this influence your decisions for this performance?

(a) Selection and rejection of ideas

....

....

....

....

....

....

(b) Responding to feedback

....

....

....

....

....

....

(c) Shaping and refining material

....

....

....

....

....

....

> Remember that you can refine material as well as your performance skills during the development process.

 Links To revise how you can develop skills and material, see pages 59–63 of the Revision Guide.

Explaining and justifying your creative decisions

It is vital to both **explain** and **justify** your decisions when completing your digital process log.

 Practise this below by writing about two recent decisions you have made while developing creative material, firstly by providing the **explanation** and secondly the **justification** (reasoning) behind the creative decisions made.

> **Guided** >
Example 1

1 Explanation

We decided that we would experiment with using only mime and mouthing words in the scene

when the homeless person visits the council.

2 Justification

We thought that this would clearly show the audience the feeling of powerlessness and difficulty

that the homeless person had in communicating their situation.

Example 2

1 Explanation

....

....

....

2 Justification

....

....

....

Example 3

1 Explanation

....

....

....

2 Justification

....

....

....

Personal management and rehearsal skills

When you write your digital process log you will need to consider your personal management and rehearsal skills.

 Answer the questions below to reflect on your own skills in relation to specific examples.

Guided 1 Complete the table below, providing **three** reasons why attendance, punctuality and meeting group and individual deadlines are crucial parts of the creative process. Then fill out the blank rows with an example of when strong skills in each area have helped you, and one way you could improve your skills in each area.

	Attendance	Punctuality	Meeting group/ individual deadlines
Reason it's important:	Builds self-discipline	Is respectful of the time of other group members	
Example of when this skills has been beneficial:			
One way you could improve in this area:			

2 How do you learn and memorise material during the rehearsal process? What helps you to remember the material, and what techniques can you use to help with this process? Provide **five** suggestions.

....

....

....

....

....

....

You will need to be able to summarise key information to support the independent judgements that you make.

51

Team skills

As part of your digital process log you, will also need to consider your team working and collaborative skills.

 Complete the spider diagram below, explaining why each of the four components are vital to the creative group process. Then give a specific example from your recent work of when you or a member of your group have shown strong skills in this area.

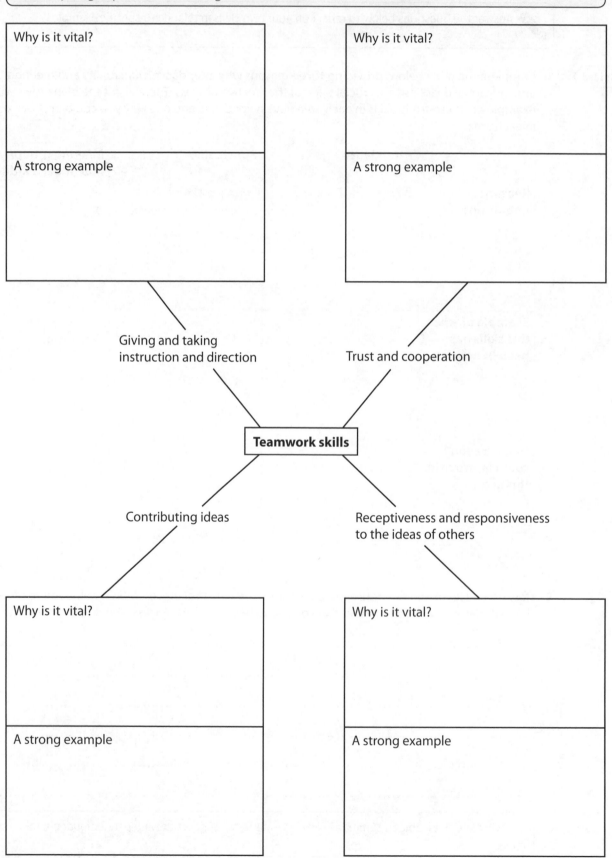

Why is it vital?

A strong example

Why is it vital?

A strong example

Giving and taking instruction and direction

Trust and cooperation

Teamwork skills

Contributing ideas

Receptiveness and responsiveness to the ideas of others

Why is it vital?

A strong example

Why is it vital?

A strong example

Review and reflect

You must be able to review and reflect on the performance and the process that led up to the performance.

> 🖉 Work through the questions on this page to ensure that you understand what this means.

1 What do you think is meant by 'review and reflect'?

....

....

2 Why are these important elements of the creative process?

....

....

....

3 When you complete your digital process log, will you be reviewing the process, the performance, or both?

....

4 Will you need to take other people's opinions into account when reviewing and reflecting? If so, whose opinions will you need to consider?

....

> **Guided** **5** You will need to consider how a performance could be developed from a 'work in progress' through to a fully resourced professional production. Note down some areas in which you could make suggestions.

The areas that might be considered are possible professional lighting ....

....

....

> **Guided** **6** Jot down some ideas about the key things you will write about in your digital process log entry, as part of the process of reviewing and reflecting on the group performance. Can you think of six examples?

I contributed ideas in the development of our performance by ....

....

....

....

....

....

....

> 🔗 **Links** To revise the different elements you can include within your review, see page 72 of the Revision Guide

Strengths and areas for improvement

Commenting on your strengths and areas for improvement for both the process as a whole and the performance itself is essential for writing your digital log.

 Complete the table below, based on some recent material you have performed.

Make judgements relating to both the process and performance.

Strength/area for improvement	Explain what it is	Why is it a strength? How can an area of weakness be improved?
Strength 1		
Strength 2		
Strength 3		
Strength 4		
Area for improvement 1		
Area for improvement 2		
Area for improvement 3		
Area for improvement 4		

 To revise processing strengths and areas for improvement, see page 72 of the Revision Guide.

Reviewing the creative process

The skills audits on the following pages will help you consider your strengths and weaknesses in a range of areas to help inform your writing of your digital log.

 Choose a recent group performance that you can use to complete the skills audit below. Circle the number that applies to your skills during the creative process and fill in the comment boxes, providing specific examples.

Skill	Rating (5 being highest)	Comments on how you could improve
Interpretation of stimulus and ideas Did you use research effectively to generate ideas? Was your experimentation with costume, props, lighting, structure and genre successful?	5 4 3 2 1	
Use of exploratory techniques Were your exploratory techniques (such as improvisation) successful?	5 4 3 2 1	
Own development and contribution of ideas Did you contribute effectively to the creative process? Could you have done more?	5 4 3 2 1	
Effectiveness of the development of own performance skills to develop and shape performance material Did you make effective decisions when developing and shaping material? Could you have pushed your creative boundaries further?	5 4 3 2 1	

Reviewing the rehearsal process

 Choose a recent group performance that you can use to complete the skills audit below. Circle the number that applies to your skills during the rehearsal process and fill in the comment boxes, providing specific examples.

Skill	Rating (5 being highest)	Comments on how to improve
Attendance and punctuality	5 4 3 2 1	
Learning and memorising material	5 4 3 2 1	
Giving and taking instruction and direction	5 4 3 2 1	
Trust and cooperation	5 4 3 2 1	
Contributing ideas	5 4 3 2 1	
Receptiveness and responsiveness to the ideas of others	5 4 3 2 1	
Participation in group tasks	5 4 3 2 1	
Commitment and focus	5 4 3 2 1	

Reviewing skills

 Choose a recent group performance that you can use to complete the audit for physical, vocal and musical skills below. Circle the number that applies to your skills during the creative process and fill in the comment boxes, providing specific examples. These can be skills shown during the development phase, or during the performance itself. If any of the skills aren't relevant to your work, cross them out and replace them with alternatives.

Skills	Rating (5 being highest)	Comments on how you could improve
Tone and pace and timing of delivery	5 4 3 2 1	
Range, pitch and intonation	5 4 3 2 1	
Articulation and projection	5 4 3 2 1	
Use of dynamics	5 4 3 2 1	
Expression and emphasis	5 4 3 2 1	
Movement and gesture	5 4 3 2 1	
Balance, alignment and posture	5 4 3 2 1	
Stamina	5 4 3 2 1	

Reviewing the effectiveness of your performance

 Choose a recent group performance that you can use to complete the skills audit below. Circle the number that applies to you and fill in the comment boxes using specific examples. Consult any notes you have taken since the performance, as well as watching the performance itself.

Skill	Rating (5 being highest)	Comments on how to improve
Effectiveness of the performance in realising the creative intention Was the intention clear? How could you have made it clearer? If you were to revisit the project, would you approach the creative intention any differently?	5 4 3 2 1	
Effectiveness of own performance skills in realising the creative intention Were your performance skills successful? How? What could you have done to improve them?	5 4 3 2 1	

Assessing audience reaction and possible future development

 Choose a recent group performance that you can use to complete the skills audit below. Circle the number which applies to you and fill in the comment boxes, using specific examples. Focus on audience feedback and potential for future development.

Skill	Rating (5 being highest)	Comments on how to improve
Development of the material (your opinion) — Were costume, props, lighting and sound successful? Would you change anything if the performance were to be a professional production?	5 4 3 2 1	
Development of the material (audience feedback) — Did the audience think the costume, props, lighting and sound were successful? Did they think it was clear what the piece was about?	5 4 3 2 1	
Development of own performance skills (your opinion) — Would your performance skills need to be developed for a professional performance? Why?	5 4 3 2 1	
Development of own performance skills (audience feedback) — Did the audience think your performance skills were successful? Did they suggest ways in which you could improve?	5 4 3 2 1	

For your assessed group performance, you could create an audience feedback sheet so that you can guide the feedback and make sure that it is constructive.

Planning and interpretation of stimulus

This section of the Workbook gives you the opportunity to record ideas and practise making notes that will be relevant for each milestone of your digital process log. You can use the revision task on page 40 as inspiration if you wish, or any other work you have recently completed.

In your digital process log you will need to describe the initial stages of the process when you first receive your stimulus (**planning** and **interpretation**). Remember it is your **own** contribution that you are writing about. Although it is a group piece, make sure that you are focusing on what **you** contributed to group discussions, meetings, research, planning, experimentation and preparation. Remember that you will be assessed on your **individual contribution** to the interpretation of the stimulus, planning and the generation of ideas.

> Use the space below to plan how you might structure and write the initial planning and interpretation of the stimulus section of your a digital process log. You can use either the given revision task or your own choice of stimulus. You are not expected to create a full process log, just to make notes or create a plan of how you could structure it and what you might include. The hints on the next pages will help you.

....
....
....
....
....
....
....
....
....
....
....
....
....
....
....
....
....
....
....
....

Remember that you can include embedded digital **photographs**, **video** and **audio** files. You may also want to include any relevant **tables**, **charts** or **diagrams**. Make a note on this page of the types of additional material you could include.

....

....

....

....

....

....

....

....

....

....

....

....

....

....

....

....

....

....

....

....

....

....

....

....

....

....

....

....

When writing your log you will need to consider: what **form** and **style** the performance will take, who the **target audience** is, how you will **communicate** your **artistic aims** and **intentions**, what **practical performance skills** you and your company can apply to the performance piece, as well as **time** and **resources** available.

....

....

....

....

....

....

....

....

....

....

....

....

....

....

....

....

....

....

....

....

....

....

....

....

....

....

....

....

Remember that you need to provide **specific examples** for every point that you make. If you are writing about exploring your stimulus, write about **how** this was done. What **methods of exploration** did you use?

....
....
....
....
....
....
....
....
....
....
....
....
....
....
....
....
....
....
....
....
....
....
....
....
....
....
....
....
....
....
....
....

Don't forget to enter the date in your digital process log for each entry.

Development of creative ideas (early stage review)

In your digital process log you will need to describe the **first part** of the creative process (**development of creative ideas**). Remember that you need to write about your **own** contribution. Although it is a group piece, make sure that you are focusing on what **you** contributed to the creative process, such as your **participation in practical activities** to **shape** and **develop** the material, **experimentation with forms and styles**, and applying **performance skills** to communicate the group's creative intention.

You will be assessed on your **exploratory techniques**, ideas for **form** and **content**, selection and development of **performance skills**, **personal management** and **collaborative skills**.

> ✏️ Use the space below to plan how you could record the development of your creative ideas in response to either the revision task on page 40 or your own choice of stimulus.

....

....

....

....

....

....

....

....

....

....

....

....

....

....

....

....

....

....

....

....

....

....

Remember that you can include embedded digital **photographs**, **video** and **audio** files. You may also want to include any relevant **tables, charts** or **diagrams**.

....
....
....
....
....
....
....
....
....
....
....
....
....
....
....
....
....
....
....
....
....
....
....
....
....
....
....
....
....

Remember that for each point you make you will need to provide **specific examples**. So if you are writing about **improvisation** in the development of motifs for example, state **how** this was done. **How** did you **shape** and **refine** material? What led you to **reject** some material? What did you contribute to the group in terms of **team skills** and **personal management**?

....

....

....

....

....

....

....

....

....

....

....

....

....

....

....

....

....

....

....

....

....

....

....

....

....

....

Don't forget to enter the date in your digital process log for each entry.

Development of creative ideas (mid-stage review)

In your digital process log you will need to describe the **mid-stage** of the creative process (**development of creative ideas**). Remember to write about your **own** contribution. Although it is a group piece, make sure that you are focusing on what **you** contributed to the creative process, such as your **participation in practical activities** to **shape** and **develop** the material, **experimentation with forms and styles** and applying **performance skills** to communicate the group's creative intention.

Remember that you will be assessed on your **exploratory techniques**, ideas for **form** and **content**, selection and development of **performance skills**, **personal management** and **collaborative skills**.

> Use the space below to plan how you could record the mid-stage of the development of your creative ideas in response to either the revision task on page 40 or your own choice of stimulus.

....

....

....

....

....

....

....

....

....

....

....

....

....

....

....

....

....

....

....

....

....

....

Remember that you can include embedded digital **photographs**, **video** and **audio** files. You may also want to include any relevant **tables**, **charts** or **diagrams**.

Remember for each point that you make, you will need to provide **specific examples**. So if you are writing about the development of your **performance skills** for example, state **how** this was done. What did you do to help develop your **performance skills**? What did you contribute to the group during the **rehearsal process**, such as **taking direction**, **receptiveness to the ideas of others** and **contributing ideas**?

....

....

....

....

....

....

....

....

....

....

....

....

....

....

....

....

....

....

....

....

....

....

....

....

....

....

....

Don't forget to enter the date in your digital process log for each entry.

Review and reflection

After you have performed as a group, you will need to reflect on the process and performance (**review** and **reflection**) by filling out the last section of your digital process log. Remember it is your **own** contribution that you are writing about. Although it is a group piece, make sure that you focus on what **you** contributed to the process and performance, what your personal **strengths** and **weaknesses** were and **how the piece could be developed** as a fully resourced professional production.

Remember that you will be assessed on your **reflection** on **personal management** and **collaborative skills**, and the **impact of your own contribution** and that of **others**, as well as your **ideas for further development of the performance**.

> Use the space below to plan how you could record your process and performance review and reflection, in response to either the revision task on page 40 or your own choice of stimulus.

....

....

....

....

....

....

....

....

....

....

....

....

....

....

....

....

....

....

....

....

....

....

Remember that you can include embedded digital **photographs**, **video** and **audio** files. You may also want to include any relevant **tables**, **charts** or **diagrams**.

....
....
....
....
....
....
....
....
....
....
....
....
....
....
....
....
....
....
....
....
....
....
....
....
....
....
....
....
....
....

Remember for each point that you make you will need to provide **specific examples**. So if you are writing about your **performance skills** and how they improved from the **process** through to **performance**, state **how** this was done. Did you undertake particular **tasks/exercises** to help improve on your weaknesses? What were they? Having watched the **recording** of the performance and taken on board **audience feedback**, **how** could the piece be **further developed**?

....
....
....
....
....
....
....
....
....
....
....
....
....
....
....
....
....
....
....
....
....
....
....
....
....
....

Don't forget to enter the date in your digital process log for each entry.

Unit 5: Individual Performance Commission

Your set task

Unit 5 will be assessed through a task, which will be set by Pearson. You will be provided with a commission brief that will include a context and purpose for the work to be produced, details of the target audience for the performance work and some constraints to work within. You will respond to the commission and stimulus, developing an individual performance for an invited audience. You will submit a proposal explaining the performance piece(s) chosen and how it relates to the brief, a video recording of your individual performance and an evaluation relating to the commission and performance work completed.

Your Revision Workbook

This Workbook is designed to **revise skills** that might be needed in your assessed task. The content, outcomes, questions and answers are provided to help you to revise content and ways of applying your skills. Ask your tutor or check the **Pearson website** for the most up-to-date **Sample Assessment Material** and **Mark Scheme** to get an indication of the structure of your assessed task and what this requires of you. When looking at the Sample Assessment Materials, you should pay attention to the details of the target audience for the performance work and time constraints, such as length of performance, number of pieces and available resources. The details of the actual assessed task may change so always make sure you are up to date.

To support your revision, this Workbook contains a revision task to help you revise skills that might be needed in your assessed task.

You will revise your skills in responding to an individual performance commission as you:

- read a commission brief and identify its purpose, the target audience and their needs, the context of the brief and any requirements and constraints (pages 76–81)
- respond to the stimulus through research and practical exploration as well as participating in a solo performance (pages 82–85 and 92–96)
- plan a written proposal in response to a commission brief, communicating your proposal with reference to the requirements of the commission brief and stimulus (pages 86–91 and 100–105)
- consider how to complete a written evaluation about the effectiveness of the final performance in response to a commission brief and selected stimulus (pages 97–99 and 106–111).

Links To help you revise skills that might be needed in your Unit 5 set task, this Workbook contains a revision task starting on page 74. See the Introduction on page iii for more information on features included to help you revise.

Revision task

To support your revision, this Workbook contains a revision task to help you revise the skills that might be needed in your assessed task. The details of the actual assessed task may change so always make sure you are up to date. Ask your tutor or check the Pearson website for the most up-to-date Sample Assessment Material.

Start by reading the revision task information, which is a commission brief from a local science museum, Sciber.

Revision task information

Although you are given a revision task below that includes a performance piece and digital process log, the Workbook will only require you to focus on the planning aspects and skills associated with the tasks involved. You are NOT expected to undertake a complete performance and associated tasks.

The commissioning body

Sciber is a local science museum which wants to promote the launch of its new building. The museum has recently been refurbished and extended so that it can showcase more exhibits, and it wants the general public to start visiting the museum again to enjoy its state-of-the-art facilities and environment.

The commission brief

Sciber is now commissioning new work for its launch in the summer. The objective is to inform the public that the museum has now reopened, as well as to promote science in education through a series of solo dance, drama, musical theatre and entertainment performances. Sciber wants to provide entertaining and stimulating experiences for its audience.

Performances may include acting, dance, musical theatre or another performance discipline such as circus skills, variety or stand-up comedy.

The work may be devised by the performer and/or developed from existing material such as a script, score or choreographic instruction, in order to meet the requirements of the commissioning body.

Target audience

The performance should appeal particularly to an audience of teenagers.

Length of performance
- The performance should run for 5–8 minutes in total.
- It could comprise a single continuous performance piece or several shorter pieces linked together.

Logistics
- This must be a solo performance.
- The performance should use only a minimum amount of technical resources, e.g. basic lighting, sound and costume.
- It should be suitable for a small indoor performance space, e.g. drama/dance studio, community hall, small theatre.

Stimulus Number One:

Scientists have found evidence of a ninth planet in the solar system which is travelling on a bizarre elongated orbit.

The body, which has been dubbed 'Planet Nine' is 10 times the mass of Earth and takes between 10,000 and 20,000 years to orbit the Sun. It is so big that researchers have branded it 'the most planety planet of the solar system.'

www.telegraph.co.uk

Stimulus Number Two:

Studying your commission brief

 The first thing you should do is to familiarise yourself with the details in the brief by reading it more than once. Use the questions below to help you identify the key information contained in the brief on page 74.

1 Referring to the commission brief on page 74, complete the following information.

(a) Type of commissioning body:

....

(b) Purpose(s) of the commissioning body:

....

....

....

(c) Objective of the commission:

....

....

....

(d) Target audience:

....

(e) Length of performance:

....

(f) Logistics:

....

....

....

....

Make sure that you keep referring back to the brief so that you can check that you are meeting the correct objective(s). There is no point in producing a spectacular performance if it does not meet the requirements of the commission brief!

 To revise types of commissioning body, see pages 82–84 of the Revision Guide.

The purpose of the commission

 Answer the questions below to help you carefully consider the purpose of the commission and how this may impact on your performance choices.

Guided **1** Outline the purpose of the commission described in the brief on page 74.

The purpose(s) of the commission is to inform the public about ....

....

.... and also to ....

....

....

2 How might the purpose(s) have an impact on the performance choices you might make?

....

....

....

....

....

....

....

....

3 Use the spider diagram to record any initial performance ideas you have based on the purpose of the commission.

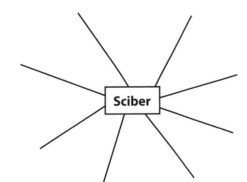

Sciber

 Links To revise why it is important to consider the purpose of the brief, see pages 85 and 86 of the Revision Guide.

Target audience

One of the requirements of the commission brief is consideration of the **target audience**. You will need to plan your performance with the target audience in mind.

> 🖋 Answer the questions on this page to help you to consider what a target audience is and how you need to plan your performance with this is mind.

1 What is a target audience?

....

....

Guided **2** Complete the spider diagram below. Write down what you need to think about when creating performance work for a target audience.

> Some target audiences might be general such as 'the public', whereas others might be quite specific, such as 'the under-5s'. It doesn't matter if your performance material appeals to people outside of your target audience, as long as your main focus addresses the needs of the target audience.

Gender

Target audience

3 Think about a piece of performance work you have created in the past for a target audience. Write down some points that you needed to consider during the preparation for the performance.

> By reflecting on your past performances you can apply any lessons learnt to any future commission briefs.

....

....

....

....

....

....

....

4 Did you succeed in meeting the requirements of the target audience? Explain why/why not.

> Be honest with yourself and consider how you apply anything you learnt in previous performances to any future commission briefs.

....

....

....

....

Needs of the target audience

Work through the questions below to help you consider the needs of the target audience in the revision activity commission brief.

Guided 1 Describe the target audience for the commission brief provided on page 74.

The target audience type is ....

and the age range is ....

The gender of the target audience is ....

Guided 2 Describe how the target audience will impact your choice of performance material.

Because the target audience type is ....

I will need to ensure that I ....

....

Regarding age, I will need to create material that ....

....

....

The gender of the target audience will mean that my performance material will need to ....

....

....

....

....

3 Can you think of difficulties that you might have in preparing performance material for your target audience, such as social and cultural issues? Make some notes about this in the space below, including how you might overcome these challenges.

....

....

....

....

....

....

....

Links To revise how you connect with your target audience, look at page 88 of the Revision Guide.

The context of the brief

In order for your performance to meet the requirements of the commission brief, you must consider the context of the brief.

> ✏️ Use the questions below to help you consider the context of the commission brief in the revision activity.

1 Explain what is meant by **context** in relation to a commission brief.

....

....

....

Guided   **2** With regard to the commission brief on page 74, complete the following information.

The objective(s) of the commission brief is ....

....

....

Guided   **3** Make a list of different forms that you could use to communicate the objective(s).

Monologue ....

....

....

Guided   **4** Describe how the type of commissioning body might affect the performance material you create.

The commissioning ....

....

....

The commissioning body's requirements might be different from those of other commissioning

bodies because ....

....

....

5 Is there a reference to past or future events in the commission brief, and can you think why this might be relevant? Jot down a few notes below.

....

....

....

....

> 🔗 **Links** To remind yourself about how to consider the context of the brief, see page 89 of the Revision Guide.

Requirements and constraints

All commissions come with requirements (things you must do) and constraints (things that limit what you are able to do).

> ✎ Work through the questions to think about the requirements and constraints of the commission brief in the revision task.

1 What is your choice of stimulus?

....

....

> Look back at page 75 to remind yourself of the choices of stimulus provided in the revision task.

Guided ⟩ **2** Give **two** considerations you must take into account for your chosen stimulus.

My choice of stimulus will mean that I need to bear in mind that ....

....

....

This will affect the choices that I make about performance material, as ....

....

....

....

....

3 Can you think of any constraints that will apply to your work resulting from your chosen stimulus?
This could include the performance space, length of performance or equipment available to you.

> Although the constraints may change as you develop your ideas later, you need to consider what may limit your performance at this stage to avoid spending time developing ideas that won't work.

....

....

....

....

4 How will you ensure that you work effectively within timescales and deadlines?

....

....

....

....

....

> You might feel restricted by not having access to a good range of facilities, but don't let that put you off. Think about how you can be creative with what you **do** have when writing your proposal, giving your performance and writing your evaluation. Elements such as costume, set, lighting and sound are additional, not essential.

Response to the stimulus

 The questions on this page will help you capture your initial responses to the stimulus to explore in more detail later.

Guided 1 Having selected one of the stimuli on page 75, jot down **ten** initial responses.

Stimulus 1

Space

....

....

....

....

....

....

....

....

....

Stimulus 2

Malfunction

....

....

....

....

....

....

....

....

....

2 Now organise your brainstorm by selecting the most significant words/phrases and discarding others, to leave you with six key points. Complete the spider diagram below.

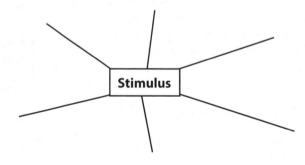

Stimulus

3 Taking the six points above, provide a suitable starting point for exploration for each one. This may be an idea to research, or a more practical method such as improvisation or hot-seating. Complete the boxes below to show starting points.

Starting point 1

Starting point 2

Starting point 3

Starting point 4

Starting point 5

Starting point 6

Research

Research is an essential part of developing a new performance.

 In this Workbook you are not expected to undertake as much research as you will for your actual assessed task as it would take too long. However, you should ensure that you have the skills you will need by spending some time looking at your chosen stimulus from the revision task on page 75 and spending at least 10-20 minutes looking for suitable sources.

Guided ⟩ Undertake some research on your stimulus from page 75, both primary and secondary if this is possible. Record your research in note form below.

Remember to **acknowledge all of your sources** as you work. Write down websites and relevant publishing details from books/journals. Don't pass off work as your own if you have taken it from another source; this counts as plagiarism and will result in you being penalised.

Stimulus 1

'For the first time in over 150 years, there is solid evidence that the solar system's planetary census is incomplete.' (www.cnet.com/news/science-is-ready-to-brawl-again-over-a-totally-different-ninth-planet/. CNET, para 7, last accessed 25 July 2017.)

....

....

....

....

....

....

Stimulus 2

'Drexel is [also] programming the robot to get into and out of a vehicle in tandem with University of Delaware researchers who are developing a way for it to drive and navigate.' (www.drexel.edu/now/archive/2013/July/DRC-HUBO-PhaseI/ para 6, last accessed 9 October 2017).

....

....

....

....

....

....

When you are recording your research, try to select only information that stands out as being interesting and relevant. This could be a statistic, a true story, an overview of the issue, an image, a quotation or part of an interview. Your research will probably be a combination of these.

Try not to rely on just one source of information; extend your search to gather information from different sources.

Practical exploration of stimulus

 Use the activities on this page to develop your ideas further. You can do this in a number of different practical ways.

Guided 1 Think about what you need to consider when you are improvising. Complete the spider diagram below with suggestions. One example has already been provided.

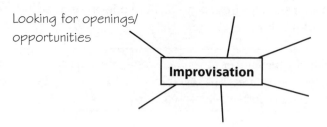

Looking for openings/ opportunities

Improvisation

Guided 2 Complete the following paragraph about how improvisation and other practical tasks can be useful during the creative process.

Improvisation means ....

....

It is useful when creating material as ....

....

....

....

It is important to try to 'think outside the box', which means ....

....

....

Other practical tasks that can help create material are ....

....

....

....

....

Using feedback from my peers enables me to ....

....

....

....

....

Remember to put your improvisation skills into practice as much as possible when developing ideas for a performance.

Developing material from your stimulus

 It is important to make links between your **stimulus** material and **commission brief**, in order to meet the assessment requirements effectively. Use the activities below to help you.

> **Guided** 1 List **five** ways that you could develop your ideas which link to your chosen stimulus and the commission brief.

Idea 1: Ninth planet article/Sciber opening – develop a monologue around the idea of living on the ninth planet, which incorporates scientific terminology that will help to educate.

Idea 2: ....

....

Idea 3: ....

....

Idea 4: ....

....

Idea 5: ....

....

> **Guided** 2 Explain why the selection of material is important when creating a performance piece.

Selection of material is important when creating performance material, as ....

....

....

....

> **Guided** 3 Explain why the rejection of material is important when creating a performance piece.

Rejection of material is also important because ....

....

....

....

> **Guided** 4 Give **three** examples of different ways of documenting your creative process.

In order to make this process easier, I make sure that I document the creative process by

....

....

....

....

....

Responding to the commission brief

> Writing a proposal is about explaining **what** you intend to do and **how** you intend to achieve this. Summarise how you will respond effectively to the commission brief. You can use the prompts given below to help you.

Guided **1** Because the target audience are teenagers, I intend to ....

....

....

....

....

....

Guided **2** As the solo needs to be 5–8 minutes long, I have decided to structure ....

....

....

....

....

....

Guided **3** As the main objectives are to inform and educate, I propose to achieve this by ....

....

....

....

....

....

Guided **4** As the solo needs to be entertaining and stimulating, I hope to ....

....

....

....

....

....

> Remember to give professional, formal responses. Be clear and concise, and refer to specific examples. Using correct grammar and spelling will help to communicate your intentions successfully.

Continue thinking about ways to respond to the commission brief by completing the questions below which encourage you to consider specific aspects of your planned performance in relation to the revision task commission brief.

> **Guided**

5 I plan on using costume to enhance my solo by wearing ....

....

....

....

....

....

> **Guided**

6 I intend to use set and lighting for my solo in order to ....

....

....

....

....

....

> **Guided**

7 Music/sound will play a significant part in my solo because ....

....

....

....

....

....

> **Guided**

8 I feel that my selected performance pathway will allow me to ....

....

....

....

....

....

Remember that for your written proposal you will be marked on your explanation of ideas in relation to the theme and stimulus. You will also need to justify your intentions in relation to all requirements of the commission brief.

Recording your stimulus responses

Your proposal should include information about your choice of stimulus.

> Justify your choice of stimulus and explain how it will affect the development of your performance.

Guided ⟩ **1** I have selected stimulus 1/2 because ....

....

....

....

Guided ⟩ **2** I have conducted primary and/or secondary research on this stimulus, which has provided

insight regarding ....

....

....

....

....

Guided ⟩ **3** To help generate material, I will perform tasks such as ....

....

....

....

....

Guided ⟩ **4** Because the target audience are teenagers, I will be able to use the stimulus to ....

....

....

....

....

....

Guided ⟩ **5** The performance material relates to the commission brief effectively, since ....

....

....

....

....

Remember to organise your proposal so that your ideas are presented in a **logical manner**. In the sentences below, show that you have considered each idea, and justify your points with examples.

Guided 6 The stimulus connects well to the Sciber Museum launch in terms of educating and informing, as

....

....

....

....

....

Guided 7 In terms of structure, I intend to ....

....

....

....

....

Guided 8 The style of the solo is going to be ....

....

which will help to communicate my intentions by ....

....

....

Guided 9 The performance skills I will need to employ are ....

....

....

I will need to use physical/vocal/music skills such as ....

....

....

....

Links For help with planning your written proposal, see page 100 of the Revision Guide.

Application of performance skills to meet the commission brief

In both your proposal and evaluation, you will need to discuss your **individual performance skills** and how they can contribute/have contributed to the given brief.

 Answer the questions on this page to ensure that you understand what performance skills are, and also how well you are able to execute them and their purpose.

Guided **1** Make a list of **ten** performance skills. One has been completed for you already.

Focus ....

....

....

....

....

2 Then select **five** performance skills which you think will be the most significant for your solo performance in response to the commission brief on page 74.

....

....

....

....

....

3 Now think about why each of the five performance skills is important to your solo performance, providing one reason for each.

....

....

....

....

....

4 Are there any ways in which you could improve these skills in preparation for your solo performance? Focus on two skills.

....

....

....

....

....

Communication of creative intentions

You will need to be very clear on your creative intention – **what your piece is about**. Throughout the creative process you will need to refer back to the objectives of the performance.

 Use the activities on this page to help you explain your creative intentions for your proposal.

Guided

1 List **five** things that you might want to communicate to an audience based on the commission brief on page 74.

Informing the public about launch of the new building ....

....

....

....

....

....

Remember that the **stimulus material** is also an important consideration. You will need to juggle the requirements of the stimulus and the commission brief throughout.

2 List **five** things that you might want to communicate to an audience based on your choice of stimulus material.

....

....

....

....

....

....

3 How could you check whether your creative intentions are clear?

....

....

....

....

....

....

You need to invest an appropriate amount of time thinking about the purpose of your performance.

Structure

When planning your performance, you must ensure that you structure your performance carefully.

> You need to ensure that you invest an appropriate amount of time into your solo performance.

> Using the revision task, make notes in response to the questions below to practise the skills involved in planning how to structure a performance.

1 Thinking about your solo in relation to the commission brief on page 74, jot down some notes about how you intend to structure it. Will you be performing one continuous piece, or a series of shorter pieces? What influenced your decision?

> Think about why you would want to perform one continuous solo; perhaps this would be preferable in terms of building tension or conveying a storyline, for example. Shorter pieces might be selected to show different moments in time or to break up different styles/shift the focus.

....

....

....

....

....

....

....

....

2 Give examples of techniques that could be used when structuring a performance of several short pieces to make it seem like a consistent performance.

> Think about the nature of the different pieces, any common themes or elements, or the transitions between them.

....

....

....

....

....

....

....

....

Use of space

Effective use of space will enhance your solo performance. It could help to add interest, establish your character or denote specific environments.

> In response to the revision task on page 74, complete the table below, stating how you intend to use space in your performance.

Use of the stage space	
Personal and general space	
Direction/pathways: diagonal, curved, meandering, forwards, backwards	
Dimensions: horizontal, vertical, sagittal	
Level: low, medium, high	

Use of props, set and costume

✎ You might want to use **props**, **set** and **costume** for your solo performance. These could help to create a mood/atmosphere, establish a character or provide a visual effect.

✎ Complete the spider diagrams and write down **five** examples of how you could use each of props, set and costumes to achieve your objectives in your performance piece.

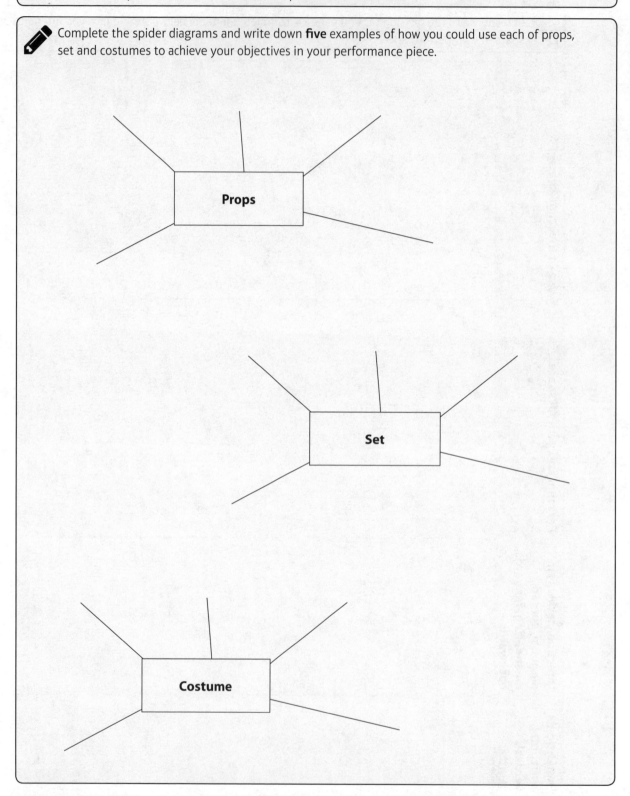

Remember that you don't have to use set, costume or props; you will not be penalised for not doing so. However, using an additional element, even if it is very basic, may help you to get into character and create the 'feel' of your piece more successfully. Don't just use a prop for the sake of it; think about **why** you are using it and if it is really necessary. Set may not be required at all; consider whether it would add anything to your performance.

Use of sound and light

Sound may already be an integral part of your solo performance, depending on your performance pathway. Think carefully when/if you are selecting music to use; check that you are not just using your favourite track for the sake of it! Sound effects could signify an environment or an era.

> ✏ Use the prompts below to consider what this could mean for the revision task.

1 Use this space to state why and how you intend to use sound in your solo performance, based on the commission brief on page 74.

....

....

....

....

....

....

....

....

....

> Even a basic wash of lighting can add an extra element to your performance. It is not a mandatory requirement but it might help you to feel more 'professional' when performing your solo.

2 Think about how lighting could enhance your solo performance. Jot down some notes below, making sure that you state why and how.

....

....

....

....

....

....

....

....

> Remember that you will not be required to incorporate extravagant lighting into your piece, so be realistic and consider simple options only.

Use of performance skills

Performance skills are essential to the performance of your solo. Depending on your selected performance pathway, some skills will be more important than others.

> ✏️ Complete the activities below to consider what this could mean for the revision task.

1 Complete the spider diagram below, stating five of the most important performance skills that you will employ. In addition, add another five performance skills that you will also need to use.

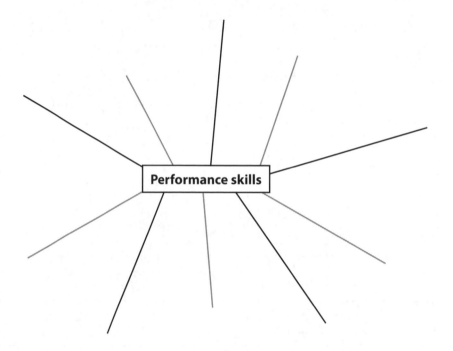

Performance skills

> **Links** Use page 106 of the Revision Guide to help you.

2 Write down why the five main skills are important to the performance of your solo.

....

....

....

....

....

3 Write down how each additional skill can enhance your solo performance.

....

....

....

....

Evaluating effectiveness of the performance work

In your actual assessed task, you will need to evaluate the effectiveness of your own performance. In this Workbook, you should select a recent piece of work of your own choosing to practice your evaluation skills.

 Complete the activity below to practise assessing the effectiveness of your performance in relation to different elements, such as clarity of interpretation.

For example, you may feel your projection is a strength but your facial expression is not so strong and you will improve this by practising specific expressions relevant for your performance in front of a mirror.

Elements to consider	Strengths	Weaknesses	How can you improve?
Solo performance skills	1 .... 2	1 .... 2	1 .... 2 ....
Clarity of interpretation	1 .... 2	1 .... 2	1 .... 2 ....
Creativity and imagination	1 .... 2	1 .... 2	1 .... 2 ....
Production values	1 .... 2	1 .... 2	1 .... 2 ....
Management of time, tasks and available resources	1 .... 2	1 .... 2	1 .... 2 ....

Conducting a skills audit

After your solo, you will need to evaluate your performance. Skills audits are a useful way of **reflecting** on your ability. For your assessment you will be completing a section in a booklet. Transferring information gained from skills audits may be useful.

 Complete the skills audit below, based on a recent solo performance. Write specific skills to consider in the first column. Circle the number that applies to you and fill in the comment boxes using specific examples. Consult any notes you have taken since the performance, as well as watching the performance itself.

Here are some examples of skills you could address in the audit: balance, coordination, alignment, flexibility, posture, stamina, pitch, tone, range, intonation, articulation, projection, use of dynamics, expression, emphasis, timing, rhythm.

Physical/vocal/ musical skill	Rating (5 being highest)	Comments on the execution of solo performance skills and how they could be developed
....	5 4 3 2 1	
....	5 4 3 2 1	
....	5 4 3 2 1	
....	5 4 3 2 1	
....	5 4 3 2 1	
....	5 4 3 2 1	
....	5 4 3 2 1	

Evaluating your ability to meet the needs of the commission brief

As part of your evaluation you will also be required to reflect on **how well you responded to the requirements** of the **stimulus** and **commission brief**.

 The questions on this page will help you to consider all the elements when writing your evaluation.

 Guided

1   Complete the spider diagram below based on some recent performance work, inputting key points that relate to each of the considerations.

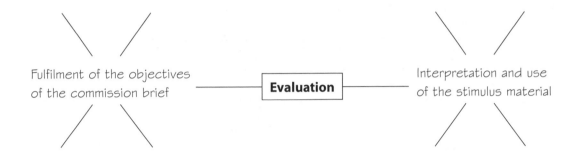

Fulfilment of the objectives
of the commission brief

Evaluation

Interpretation and use
of the stimulus material

 Links   To revise the skills involved in evaluating your success in meeting a commission brief, see page 116 of the Revision Guide.

2   Expand on the key points from your spider diagram, providing additional explanation and examples to illustrate your points.

....

....

....

....

....

....

....

....

....

....

....

....

Proposal: introduction

This section of the Workbook is based on the commission brief on page 74. Use the work you have completed on pages 86–91 to construct a written proposal in relation to the brief.

 Use the next six pages to write a proposal for the commission brief given on page 74. You can use the hints given on each page to help you structure your proposal.

Your proposal should be clear, concise and well organised, using correct spelling and grammar throughout. A confident, professional approach should be conveyed.

It is a good idea to make a plan of what you want to include in each paragraph before starting to write. Begin your proposal by introducing your main objectives, which you will develop in the main body of the proposal. Use the space below for the introduction.

....
....
....
....
....
....
....
....
....
....
....
....
....
....
....
....
....
....
....

If you are writing a proposal in your assessment, you may need to write to a word limit, for example 1000 words. Ask your tutor or check the Pearson website for the most up-to-date Sample Assessment Material and Mark Scheme to make sure you have the latest information.

Proposal: researching the commission brief and stimulus

Use the space below to show that you have researched ideas relating to the commission brief, as well as the stimulus. Use **specific examples** when you are making points, as well as stating **why** you have reached certain decisions. Remember to acknowledge any websites you have used, to avoid being penalised for plagiarism.

....

....

....

....

....

....

....

....

....

....

....

....

....

....

....

....

....

....

....

....

....

....

....

....

....

Proposal: requirements and constraints

On this page you should demonstrate awareness of the **requirements** and **constraints** of the commission brief, as well as how the commission brief relates to the stimulus. Also, try to be realistic when writing about your aims and intentions; remember that you will need to consider the available resources.

....

....

....

....

....

....

....

....

....

....

....

....

....

....

....

....

....

....

....

....

....

....

....

....

....

Proposal: justifying intentions and addressing target audience

On this page you can **explain** and **justify your intentions and ideas** in relation to the commission brief, theme and stimulus. Make sure that you show an understanding of the **purpose** of the commission, as well as how you can create performance work for a particular **target audience**.

Proposal: generating material

On this page you should explain how you plan to **generate material** for performance, such as through improvisational tasks. Show that you understand the **type of commissioning body** and how this will affect your solo performance; this may require some research.

....

....

....

....

....

....

....

....

....

....

....

....

....

....

....

....

....

....

....

....

....

....

....

....

....

....

Proposal: conclusion

Draw your proposal to a close by **summarising your intentions**.

....
....
....
....
....
....
....
....
....
....
....
....
....
....
....
....
....
....
....
....
....
....
....
....
....
....
....
....

Evaluation: clarity of interpretation

In this section of the Workbook, you are given an opportunity to practise your extended written evaluation skills. As creating a solo performance in response to the revision task would not be practical, you are invited to plan and write an evaluation based on a recent solo performance of your own choice.

> Over the next few pages, use the work you completed on pages 97–99 to help you in planning and practising writing an evaluation. Remember to cover all of the necessary elements in your evaluation, in addition to how well you executed solo performance skills. An important element is **clarity of interpretation**. With reference to a recent solo performance, discuss **how** you made things clear, and **what/how** you could have improved. Feedback from peers, your teacher or the audience will be useful here.

....
....
....
....
....
....
....
....
....
....
....
....
....
....
....
....
....
....
....
....
....

> If you are writing an evaluation in your assessment, you may need to write to a word limit, for example 1500 words. Ask your tutor or check the Pearson website for the most up-to-date Sample Assessment Material and Mark Scheme to make sure you have the latest information.

Evaluation: creativity and use of imagination

Include discussion of your **creativity** and how well you exercised your **imagination in relation to a previous solo you have performed**. Could your performance have been more original? How did you use tasks to create material for your solo?

....
....
....
....
....
....
....
....
....
....
....
....
....
....
....
....
....
....
....
....
....
....
....
....
....

Evaluation: production values

Remember to discuss your **production values in relation to a recent performance**. How well did you use **costume**, **lighting**, **sound**, **set** and **props** to enhance your solo performance?

Evaluation: managing time and resources

Discuss how effectively you managed **your time**, **tasks** and **available resources, based on a recent solo performance**. Did you find it more or less challenging than working in a group? Why was this?

....

....

....

....

....

....

....

....

....

....

....

....

....

....

....

....

....

....

....

....

....

....

....

....

....

....

....

Evaluation: fulfilling the commission brief

An important part of your evaluation will be to explore how effectively you fulfilled the **objectives** of the **commission brief**. In relation to a recent solo performance, consider how you adapted your material to meet the **requirements** and **constraints** of the task. Did you meet the objectives successfully? If not, why not?

....

....

....

....

....

....

....

....

....

....

....

....

....

....

....

....

....

....

....

....

....

....

....

....

Evaluation: use of stimulus

Another significant part of your evaluation will be to discuss how effectively you **used** and **interpreted** the **stimulus** material. Did you **research** the stimulus successfully? Did the material you created using the stimulus **relate appropriately to the commission brief**?

Unit 7: Employment opportunities in the Performing Arts

Your set task

Unit 7 will be assessed through a task, which will be set by Pearson. You will need to use your understanding of performing arts organisations and the employment opportunities they provide, and present a response to a potential employment opportunity, gathering and presenting evidence to support your application.

Your Revision Workbook

> This Workbook is designed to **revise skills** that might be needed in your assessed task. The content, outcomes, questions and answers are provided to help you revise content and ways of applying your skills. Ask your tutor or check the **Pearson website** for the most up-to-date **Sample Assessment Material** and **Mark Scheme** to get an indication of the structure of your assessed task and what this requires of you. Make sure you check the instructions in relation to what may be needed for completion on computer, and whether PDFs and embedded digital files may be needed. The details of the actual assessed task may change, so always make sure you are up to date.

To support your revision, this Workbook contains two revision tasks to help you revise the skills that might be needed in your assessed task.

You will revise your skills in responding to a potential employment opportunity as you:

- read an example employment opportunity, understand what constitutes the organisation and interpret the project requirements (pages 113–116 and 133–136)
- identify the skills and experience the opportunity requires and demonstrate how your skills and experience are suitable to take part in the project and lead workshops (pages 117–121 and 137–138)
- plan and evaluate workshop ideas in relation to the opportunity, describing and justifying a selected idea in response to requirements (pages 122 and 139)
- prepare and select evidence for your promotional portfolio by:
  - considering ways to select and structure evidence that best demonstrate your skills and experience in relation to the opportunity (pages 127–129 and 142–143)
  - considering ways to select effective extracts of practical work that might include video clips, audio recordings, photographs and other supporting material (pages 130–132 and 144)
- revise your ability to demonstrate clear, effective and persuasive promotional intent in your written response, and ways to structure a relevant response that justifies your suitability (pages 123–126 and 140–141).

> **⚿ Links** To help you revise skills that might be needed in your Unit 7 set task, this Workbook contains two revision tasks starting on pages 113 and 133. The first is guided and models good techniques, to help you develop your skills. The second gives you the opportunity to apply the skills you have developed. See the Introduction on page iii for more information on features included to help you revise.

Revision task 1

To support your revision, this Workbook contains two revision tasks to help you revise the skills that might be needed in your assessed task. This first one guides you through how to approach the task with activities; the second is for you to work through more independently. The details of the actual assessed task may change so always make sure you are up to date. Ask your tutor or check the Pearson website for the most up-to-date Sample Assessment Material.

In this first revision task, you are asked to consider the revision task information provided, and work through the activities to help you in **planning** a **written response** that justifies your suitability to offer a workshop as part of 'shortWIRED's upcoming tour. This will involve your understanding of what constitutes the organisation and details of the skills and experience you can offer and how these will inform the workshop activities you are proposing.

You are also asked to plan towards preparing a **promotional portfolio** that provides evidence of your skills and experience, with extracts of practical work to support your application for a job role in 'shortWIRED'. The skills and experience you select for inclusion in your self-promotional portfolio should be those best suited for the organisational profile, project and workshop.

Revision task information

Start by reading the task information with the details of the opportunity being offered, organisational profile, project outline and workshop requirements.

shortWIRED: Employment Opportunity

We are looking for workshop leaders from a range of disciplines to join our vibrant company for a national tour. Singers, dancers, actors and circus performers are all welcome to apply.

You are required to demonstrate your understanding of our organisation and how you can contribute to the work we do and what you plan to deliver in the workshop, using relevant examples to justify your ideas and skills. It is essential that you consider the age and profile of the group your workshop will target.

Organisational Profile

shortWIRED is a hard-hitting physical theatre company that produces challenging and original works for young audiences of 14+. Our aim is to push the boundaries of our audiences, presenting them with different perspectives on serious social issues. Past performances have explored teen pregnancy, asylum seekers and personal identity. We are passionate about presenting alternative points of view and opening young people's minds to difference and acceptance.

We are funded mainly by the Arts Council England. Part of our funding is allocated to provide free workshops to schools in the areas that we perform in. All of our performers design and lead these workshops, based on the piece we create.

Project Outline

The working title of the project is 'Poor on the inside' and our performers will work collaboratively with the artistic director and our design team to create new and exciting theatre that is inclusive of everyone. It will further young people's understanding of what makes us 'poor on the inside' and how this can affect our everyday lives. Multidisciplinary experience is desirable, but we are more interested in finding individuals who bring something new to the rehearsal space.

Workshop Requirements

We aim to offer a workshop in addition to the performance outlined above. This will extend the understanding of the themes, ideas and concepts within the project. The workshop needs to be inclusive, fun and have clear objectives. We would like you to propose ideas for a workshop as part of your submission. We are looking for a talented individual to lead and develop this.

The organisation

To create a successful response to an employment opportunity, you need to fully understand the organisation offering the opportunity.

> 🖉 Complete the following notes about the organisation, with reference to the brief on page 113.

1 Using the revision task brief, identify **three** of the aims of shortWIRED.

....

....

....

2 Using the revision task brief, identify **three** of the objectives of shortWIRED.

....

....

....

> Guided

3 Underline or highlight words or phrases from the brief that describe the company:

> Highlight words that provide insight into the company, e.g. challenging.

> shortWIRED is a hard-hitting physical theatre company that produces challenging and original works to young audiences of 14+. Our aim is to push the boundaries of our audiences, presenting them with different perspectives on serious social issues. Past performances have explored teen pregnancy, asylum seekers and personal identity. We are passionate about presenting alternative points of view and opening young people's minds to difference and acceptance.

4 Using the words you have underlined or highlighted, write down what you think are the vision, mission and values of shortWIRED.

Vision:

....

Mission:

....

Values:

....

> 🎧 **Links** To revise consideration of the aims, objectives and values of an organisation, see pages 121–123 of the Revision Guide.

Organisational profile: audience

You need to fully understand the audience that the organisation is targeting, in order to create a successful response to an employment opportunity.

 Extract information from the revision task brief to answer the following questions.

Guided 1 Who is shortWIRED's intended audience? Identify **three** types of people and write them in the left column.

Be specific.

Intended audiences	Reasons shortWIRED will appeal
People interested in serious social issues	

2 Using the right-hand column of the table above, write a reason why you think shortWIRED will appeal to each intended audience.

Guided 3 For each of the stakeholders listed below, give a reason why they would be important to shortWIRED.

People coming to the performance:...

....

The community:...

....

Artistic director: Because their guidance would help to produce challenging work that pushes

boundaries. ....

....

The Arts Council:...

....

The performers:...

....

4 What is the geographical scope of shortWIRED? Circle the answer.

Local   Regional   National   International

5 What would this mean to the performers who go on tour?

....

Organisational profile: funding

You are more valuable to an organisation if you understand how it operates. Consider how an organisation gets its funding so you can demonstrate that you are the best person for the opportunity they are offering.

> 🖊 Using the revision task brief, answer the following questions.

1 What sort of organisation do you think shortWIRED is? Circle your answer.

Unincorporated association   Company limited by guarantee

Sole trader   Charity   Company limited by shares

Community interest company   Industrial provident society

2 Name **two** potential sources of funding for this type of organisation.

....

Guided **3** List **six** possible tasks that this type of funding body might ask shortWIRED to do as part of their funding agreement.

Take photos of the workshops.

....

....

....

....

....

Guided **4** Identify the skills needed to complete each task, and note down whether or not you have the skill.

Task	Skill needed to do the task	Do you have the skill?
Take photos of the workshops	Photography	Yes/No
		Yes/No
		Yes/No
		Yes/No

> 🔗 **Links** See pages 129–132 of the Revision Guide for help on funding bodies.

Skills required

 Do you have the right skills for the job? Using the revision task brief on page 113, consider the skills the job requires.

Guided **1** What skills and qualities do you think shortWIRED is looking for in a workshop leader? Write your ideas in this spider diagram.

> Remember to include both performance skills (to help you plan and lead a workshop) as well as work skills shortWIRED may be looking for.

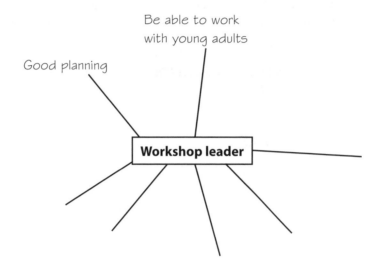

2 Using the spider diagram, list the skills you think are the most important for shortWIRED, that you will focus on in your written response and digital portfolio.

> Make sure you refer back to the revision task and focus on the most important skills.

....

....

....

....

....

....

Links Refer to page 140 in the Revision Guide for a list of possible skills.

Your skills

Once you have considered what skills the employment opportunity requires, consider how your own skills, qualities and experience match the requirements.

 Use the questions below to assess your own skills in relation to the revision task on page 113. You will have a wide range of skills that cover both performance and work, so consider them all.

Guided 1 Make a list of your own skills in the table below. Evaluate whether shortWIRED would want you to have this skill. Identify the best way to evidence it.

> Draw from your own experience to produce evidence for your written response. Good forms of evidence within your promotional portfolio could be audio recordings, video recordings, your CV, certificates, reviews. You can evidence a skill more than once.

My skills	Relevant to shortWIRED?	Best way to evidence it
Interpersonal skills	YES/~~NO~~	Clip of me leading a choreography session
	YES/NO	
	YES/NO	
	YES/NO	
	YES/NO	
	YES/NO	
	YES/NO	
	YES/NO	

2 Using the table above and your responses on the previous page, identify which skills you will focus on in your written response and digital portfolio, along with evidence.

....

....

....

....

....

....

> **Links** Refer to page 140 in the Revision Guide for a list of possible skills.

Your qualities

Your personal qualities are important to consider when thinking about your fit to a role or organisation. You need to be honest with yourself in considering any evidence of personal qualities that could be important.

 Use the activities below to assess your personal qualities in relation to the revision task brief on page 113.

Use the activities below to assess your personal qualities in relation to the revision task brief on page 113.

Guided 1 Brainstorm your personal qualities. Fill in the spider diagram below.

Personal qualities can include all sorts of things, such as being an extrovert or introvert, being a perfectionist, being laid back or very driven, being empathetic, flexible, being energetic, and having a positive attitude. You can probably think of more! You can add more arms to the spider diagram.

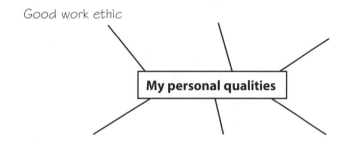

Good work ethic

My personal qualities

Guided 2 Choose six of the personal qualities you have listed that are most relevant to the values of shortWIRED referring back to the revision task brief. List them below and give an example from your experience that supports each quality.

Personal quality	Where have I applied this quality?
Perfectionist	In my group choreography, 'Miles Apart'

3 From the table above, choose one personal quality and write a few sentences as part of a written response.

You need to give the personal quality, state the evidence for it and ensure that you link this back to the organisation and employment opportunity.

....

....

....

....

....

Your perfomance experience

You need to consider specific examples of your performance experience and link them to what the organisation requires.

 Use the activities below to select performance experiences that are relevant to the revision task brief on page 113.

on page 113.

Guided 1 Make a list of your performance experience in the table below. Rate each experience for the following.
- Quality: how good was your performance?
- Suitability: does your performance experience fit the employment opportunity?

Grade the quality and suitability out of 10 (10 = very strong, 1 = not strong at all).

Performance	Quality	Suitability
Extracts from 'Waiting for Godot'	6	7

2 Using the table, select the most appropriate performances to discuss in your written response. Which skills do they show?

....

....

....

....

....

> The examples you choose for your written response should appear in written form (e.g. a script you have written) or you can describe clearly in writing. They should be both high quality and relevant.

3 Using the table, select the most appropriate performances to include in your digital promotional portfolio. What skills do they show?

....

....

....

....

....

> The examples you choose for your digital portfolio should be those which include evidence that can best be shown through video, photo or audio, such as facial expressions, intonation or complex choreography. They should be high quality and relevant.

Other experience

You need to consider specific examples of your work experience and link them to what the organisation requires.

 Use the activities below to select work experiences that are relevant to the revision task brief on page 113.

1 Make a list of any part-time jobs or voluntary work you have done.

Your job   **Voluntary or paid**

1 ....

2 ....

3 ....

4 ....

5 ....

Guided ▷ **2** Against each employability skill in the table below, insert the number of the job from the list above where you would have used the skill and then write a short description of how you applied that skill in the job.

Employability skill	Job (no.)	Applying the skill
Numeracy skills	1	Handling money, calculating change
Interpersonal skills		
Critical thinking skills		
Presentation skills		
IT skills		
Literacy skills		
Leadership skills		
Teamwork		
Personal motivation		
Personal organisation		
Time management		
Listening skills		

Workshop ideas

The employment opportunity in the revision task on page 113 asks you to provide ideas for workshops as part of your written response.

 Use the approach shown here to identify your ideas for workshops.

> **Guided**

1 Brainstorm some workshop ideas for the theme 'Poor on the inside'.

At this stage focus on 'big picture' ideas, so your responses should just be one or two words. You will expand on these later.

Loneliness

Poor on the inside

2

> Our aim is to push the boundaries of our audiences, presenting them with different points of view of serious social issues. Past performances have explored teen pregnancy, asylum seekers and personal identity. We are passionate about presenting alternative points of view and opening young people's minds to difference and acceptance.

Evaluate your ideas and select one idea that best suits the aim of shortWIRED from looking back at page 113 and page 114.

Selected idea:..

3 Write a short description of the workshop idea, ensuring that you clearly link your idea to the aims of shortWIRED given above. Make sure you consider the objective of the workshop.

You will expand on this in more detail on page 126. Here, you should give a description of the objective and content of the workshop, as well as explaining how it links to the aims of the organisation.

....

....

....

....

....

....

Written response: introduction practice

Your written response needs to demonstrate clear, effective and persuasive promotional intent, this means showing how your skills, ideas and experience are relevant to the organisation and the job description given. Use the pages that follow to practise your skills in doing this.

> Start with an introductory section that clearly sets out who you are and why you feel your skills and experience are a good fit to the opportunity described.

1 Write a few sentences to introduce yourself to the organisation. Include your name and your chosen profession (dancer, singer, actor, for example).

> Use full sentences and think about your grammar in all your written work.

....

....

....

Guided **2** Briefly describe the employment opportunity in your own words.

> Go back to the job description and read it again if you need to.

I believe you are looking for ....

....

....

Guided **3** Briefly identify your most relevant, recent experience and why it makes you a good candidate.

> Don't go into depth here. This section just gives the employer an idea of your background. You will discuss your key skills and their relevance in more depth later. Make sure you focus on what connects you with the employment opportunity.

I am currently ....

....

....

4 Write any additional reasons you have for being interested in the employment opportunity. This could be to do with the organisation's vision, ethos, values, etc.

....

....

....

....

> **Links** To revise effective written communication skills, see page 143 in the Revision Guide. You can find out more about promotional intent on page 151 of the Revision Guide.

Written response: your skills

You will need to make sure that you clearly link your skills and personal experience with the opportunity described.

 Using your answers on page 118, choose examples that describe and give evidence in relation to a workshop leader. Then write a section of your written response which focuses on the skills that make you suited to the role by completing the activities below.

Guided **1** Describe your skills as a performer that will help you to operate in the company as a workshop leader. Ensure you give evidence, outlining when and how you used these skills, as in the example below.

I am able to develop characters through research and exploration. When performing in 'A place called home', a physical theatre piece that explored issues of homelessness, I spent an evening sleeping rough with the company so that we could fully appreciate how exposing it is and how it

would affect us in the piece. ....

....

....

....

....

....

....

....

2 You must make sure that the examples you describe are linked to what the organisation is looking for. Write a paragraph that does this. You should also use subject-specific terminology like the learner below.

I would be able to lead a workshop that either included a similar experience or else show workshop participants images from my experience to help develop their ideas relating to mental and physical

health in performance work for 'Poor on the inside'. ....

....

....

....

....

....

....

....

....

....

Written response: additional skills

In addition to your performance skills, you will have other personal qualities and skills that are relevant to the opportunity.

 Use your notes on pages 119–121 to write a section from your written response in which you explain what your additional skills are, provide evidence of these and explain how they are linked to the opportunity.

Guided

1 Write a few sentences about your skills similar to the ones by the student below.

I have experience of writing evaluations of workshops, having completed this as part of my BTEC National course assessment. This will help in evidencing the workshops myself and others at shortWIRED carry out in order to gain funding from the Arts Council England.

....

....

....

....

....

....

....

....

....

....

Guided

2 Finally, summarise your own values and how these relate to shortWIRED's values.

I am a .... person and I believe that these qualities

reflect/match your values of ....

.... This will mean that as a workshop leader

with shortWIRED I can ....

....

....

....

....

....

....

....

Refer back to pages 113–116 of this Workbook and consider anything the organisation might ask you to do in addition to the workshop leader role.

Written response: workshop ideas

You need to clearly communicate your workshop ideas, ensuring that these are linked to the task brief and the organisational purpose and structure.

 Using the ideas you developed on page 122, answer the questions below to help you structure and present your workshop ideas as part of a written response.

Guided 1 First introduce a few key ideas you have had, and explain why they are relevant by linking them to the aims of shortWIRED and the workshop requirements.

> Include approximately four different ideas to demonstrate breadth of creative thinking.

I have several ideas for the workshops. These include ....

....

....

....

....

....

....

....

Guided 2 Identify which idea you think is most suitable and explain why.

> Relate the idea to the aims, objectives, mission, vision and values of shortWIRED.

The idea I feel most suits your organisation is ....

because ....

....

....

Guided 3 Write an objective for your workshop idea.

By the end of the workshop the participants will have ....

....

Guided 4 Describe your workshop in more detail.

The workshop will start with ....

....

It will then move on to ....

....

It will end with ....

....

Structuring your promotional portfolio

When planning your digital promotional portfolio, consider what evidence will best demonstrate your skills and experience in relation to the opportunity. Your extracts of practical work might include video clips, audio recordings, photographs and other supporting materials. In response to the revision task brief on page 113, use the following pages to plan what you might include in your portfolio and why, and how best to structure it.

> There may be restrictions on what evidence and how much content you can include in your portfolio. Ask your tutor or check the Pearson website for the most up-to-date **Sample Assessment Material** and **Mark Scheme** to make sure you have the latest information.

> **Guided** | Use the boxes on this page to plan each of the sections of your promotional portfolio. Write a heading for the section in each box. Make sure the sections are in a logical order. Each section may be made up of one or more pages.

> You must make sure that you effectively evidence the skills you identified as relevant to the opportunity on pages 117–121. You should ensure that:
> - you have chosen the best examples of evidence - where your skills appear strongest
> - you are presenting it in a logical order for an employer who doesn't know anything about your experience
> - you have made it clear how each piece of evidence is relevant (what skills it shows)
> - you use high quality digital content (avoid blurring or footage where you can't be seen clearly).

Short introduction to my promotional portfolio, including my CV and any key stats about myself	....	....
....	....	....
....	....	....

 Links To revise promotional portfolio components, see page 145 of the Revision Guide.

The promotional portfolio: planning

 Use the space here to help plan what evidence you will include on each page of your portfolio and plan a conclusion for your promotional portfolio, that is consistent with the ideas expressed in your written response.

Guided 1 Write a list of contents.

> Use your portfolio structure from page 127 to help you.

Page 1   Introduction

Page 2   CV with headshot

Page 3   ....

Page ....

Page ....

Page ....

Page ....

Page ....

Page ....

Page ....

Page ....

2 Write a short conclusion to be placed at the end of your portfolio.

> Consider the following questions.
> - Can the potential employers contact you for additional video links?
> - Can you post links to websites of the companies you have worked with so far?
> - Can you list additional references for the organisation to contact?

....

....

....

....

....

....

....

....

....

....

....

....

....

The promotional portfolio: your CV

When creating your digital portfolio, you need to consider ways to make it relevant, show promotional intent and use your analysis skills to critically select good examples to include. The pages that follow use selected parts of your portfolio to revise your skills in doing this.

 Start by considering how you might present a CV if you are asked for one, along with your head and body shots. There are different ways you can present this, so although one example is given below, you could choose an alternative layout. Complete the example below to create a CV appropriate for the revision task given on page 113.

You could word process your CV and save it as a PDF. For what is needed in your actual assessment, see the Sample Assessment Material on the Pearson website.

Full name: ....

Address: ....

Home contact number: ....

Mobile contact number: ....

Email address: ....

[Insert a copy of your head shot here]

Height: .... Hair: ....

Build: .... Eye colour: ....

Training

Years	School/College	Full qualification title
.... –	....	....
.... –	....	....

Make sure that you tailor your CV to the opportunity you are applying for. The skills, credits and experience you list here should tie in with the work you have already done in identifying what is relevant for this specific opportunity.

Additional Skills

....

....

Credits

Year	Type	Role	Production Company	Director
....	....	....	....	....
....	....	....	....	....

Additional Experience

....

....

The promotional portfolio: audio evidence

If you use audio evidence as part of your portfolio, ensure that your selection(s) are relevant and consistent with your written response.

 Use the activity below to revise your skills when selecting appropriate audio files and writing about them for your promotional portfolio.

In your actual assessment you may need to embed your audio evidence in a PDF. If so, make sure you are familiar with embedding files and what is required of you. Ask your tutor or look at the Sample Assessment Material on the Pearson website for more details.

1 Either select a short audio clip from your existing performance recordings, or create one that shows a skill that you identified as relevant to the employment opportunity in the revision task on page 113. You should consider the following points when selecting an audio file:

- Does it clearly show evidence of one or more skills that the organisation is looking for?
- Is it an appropriate length? Check the total length of video and audio evidence permitted with your tutor, or on the Pearson website.
- Is the quality good enough?
- Is the file type one that can be submitted?

2 Write a few short sentences to describe the content of the audio file. Use the following questions to help you structure your writing.

(a) What is the audio clip?

A clip of .... from my performance

of .... showing how ....

....

(b) Who is in the clip? Ensure you identify which speaker is you.

....

....

(c) When did the recording take place? ....

(d) Write one or two sentences identifying the skill(s) shown and why they are relevant.

....

....

....

....

....

The promotional portfolio: video evidence

If you use video evidence as part of your portfolio, ensure that your selection(s) are relevant and consistent with your written response.

 Use the activity below to revise your skills when selecting and writing about appropriate video files for your promotional portfolio.

In your actual assessment you may need to embed your video evidence in a PDF. If so, make sure you are familiar with embedding files and what is required of you. Ask your tutor or look at the Sample Assessment Material on the Pearson website for more details.

1 Either select a short video clip from your existing performance recordings or create a short clip that shows a skill that you identified as relevant to the employment opportunity earlier in this unit. You should consider the following points when selecting a video clip:

- Does it clearly show evidence of one or more skills that the organisation is looking for?
- Is it an appropriate length? Check the total length of video and audio evidence permitted with your tutor, or on the Pearson website.

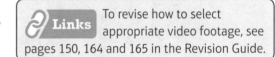 **Links** To revise how to select appropriate video footage, see pages 150, 164 and 165 in the Revision Guide.

- Is the quality good enough?
- Is the file type one that can be submitted?

Guided 2 Write a few short sentences to describe the content of the video. Use the following questions to help you structure your writing.

(a) What is the video clip?

This video clip shows ....

....

(b) Who is performing? Explain how to identify you in the video.

....

....

....

You could give a physical description of yourself (e.g. hair colour, clothing), describe your positioning (e.g. 'I am on the right of the video') or describe what you are doing (e.g. 'I am carrying a jug').

(c) What date was the performance?

....

(d) What was your role in the video? (Performer/director/choreographer/workshop leader)

....

(e) Write one or two sentences identifying the skill(s) shown and techniques you used and why they are relevant.

....

....

You should make sure that you clearly link this with the skills you have identified the organisation is looking for.

....

....

The promotional portfolio: additional evidence

You may wish to include additional evidence in your portfolio. This might be photos, letters, posters, or certificates for example. These should be clearly relevant to the organisation and/or workshop requirements. Consider the following points when selecting additional evidence:

* Is the quality good enough?
* Is the file type one that can be submitted?
* Does it clearly show evidence of one or more skills that the organisation is looking for?
* Have you made clear in your description how the evidence links to the skills needed?

> Use the activity below to consider at least three pieces of other evidence you could include in relation to the revision task on page 113. Make sure you give details of each piece of evidence and how it links to the skills needed in the employment opportunity.

Guided

1

Photo of me (on the left) leading a workshop with children at my local school. This photo shows my ability to engage children which will be helpful for leading workshops for shortWIRED.

2

....

....

....

....

3

....

....

....

....

4

....

....

....

....

> Although you need to give details about most pieces of evidence in your portfolio (like the pieces above), items like head shots, CVs and references won't normally need explanation and will just need to be embedded into your portfolio document.

Revision task 2

To support your revision, this Workbook contains two revision tasks to help you revise the skills that might be needed in your assessed task. In this second revision task, you have the opportunity to respond to a different task brief using the skills you have practised so far. The details of the actual assessed task may change so always make sure you are up to date. Ask your tutor or check the Pearson website for the most up-to-date Sample Assessment Material.

You have been asked to present a written response and digital promotional portfolio for the employment opportunity being offered by the Heritage Theatre, a performing arts organisation.

Revision task information

The Heritage Theatre: Employment Opportunity

We are looking for an enthusiastic and creative workshop leader, to join our small team. Our workshop leaders are the public face of the company and it is their excellence that enables the continued success of the Heritage Theatre.

You are required to demonstrate your understanding of our organisation, how you can contribute to the work we do and what you plan to deliver in the workshop, using relevant examples to justify your ideas and skills.

It is essential that you consider the age and profile of the group your workshop will target.

Organisational Profile

We are a small local community interest company, which runs a highly successful outreach programme to local homes for elderly people. Our aim is to engage the older generation in performing arts through workshops and activities. We work with a number of care homes, creating an individualised experience for their residents focusing on engagement, participation, energy and fun. This includes, but is not restricted to, workshops in a wide variety of disciplines, vaudeville-style entertainment within the care home and trips to the Heritage Theatre.

We are funded mainly by service-level agreements with the different care homes in the area, and we work hard to build and maintain our portfolio. This involves developing more contacts with local businesses and providers. The outreach department also develops and plans the workshops, whether they are one-off performances, a series of regular workshops or a residency. All members of our outreach team contribute to these aspects of the job.

Project Outline

We are looking to develop more long-term contracts with care homes in the local area. To do this we need a team of passionate workshop leaders who can plan and deliver high-quality workshops. This latest project uses the performing arts to explore the theme of 'Back in the day'. The immersive experience enables elderly people to explore their memories, and life experiences. All our work is mindful of the limitations of working in non-theatrical space and how activities need to be adapted to different levels of mobility.

Workshop Requirements

The workshop must be suitable for the age of the participants and cater for their needs. The workshop needs to be inclusive, fun and have clear objectives. We would like you to propose ideas for a workshop as part of your submission. We are looking for a talented individual to lead and develop this.

The organisation

You should always take time to consider the different aspects of the brief. The first aspect of the brief you should consider is the nature of the organisation advertising the employment opportunity.

> Use the space below to make notes, demonstrating that you understand the aims, objectives, vision, mission and values of the organisation offering the employment opportunity.

....

....

....

....

....

....

....

....

....

....

....

....

....

....

....

....

....

....

....

....

....

....

....

....

....

Organisational profile: audience

You also need to think about what the brief tells you about the audience of the project and workshop.

> In the space below, make notes demonstrating your understanding of the intended audience of the project and workshops. Think about **who** the audience is, **what** it is about the project that appeals to the intended audience, and **who** the stakeholders involved with the project are.

....

....

....

....

....

....

....

....

....

....

....

....

....

....

....

....

....

....

....

....

....

....

....

....

....

....

....

Organisational profile: funding

Next you should think about the nature of the funding for the organisation.

> On this page you should make notes regarding the type of organisation the Heritage Theatre is, where it gets its funding from and where it could secure more funding. Make sure you consider how the nature of the funding affects the type of information you should include in your written response.

....

....

....

....

....

....

....

....

....

....

....

....

....

....

....

....

....

....

....

....

....

....

....

....

....

....

Skills and techniques: professional practice

Make sure you think about the skills and techniques the employer is looking for.

In the space below, you should detail the skills and qualities that the Heritage Theatre is looking for in a workshop leader. Look carefully at the revision task brief and think about the opportunity in the context of your chosen performance pathway. Then think about how you can demonstrate these skills and techniques, providing concrete examples of your experience.

....

....

....

....

....

....

....

....

....

....

....

....

....

....

....

....

....

....

....

....

....

....

....

....

....

....

Skills and qualities: employability

Think about appropriate evidence for your wider employability skills such as leadership or team building.

On this page you should use the space below to detail the employability skills and personal qualities the Heritage Theatre is looking for. How can you demonstrate these skills and techniques, providing concrete examples of your experience? You need to consider how you fit what they are looking for.

....

....

....

....

....

....

....

....

....

....

....

....

....

....

....

....

....

....

....

....

....

....

....

....

....

....

....

Workshop requirements

Within your written response you will need to provide your ideas for the workshop with reference to the project requirements.

> In the space below, brainstorm some workshop ideas and opportunities for the Heritage Theatre. Consider one-off performances, regular workshops and residencies.

....

....

....

....

....

....

....

....

....

....

....

....

....

....

....

....

....

....

....

....

....

....

....

....

....

....

Practise your written response

Your full written response in your assessment will be created under supervised assessment conditions over a specified period of time. You will need to have a clear plan for your response before you start writing.

> ✎ Use the space below to create a plan for your written response for the revision task, using the notes you have made on page 134–139. Your written response should be **clear**, **concise** and **well organised**. Go back to the task brief on page 133 to remind yourself of the job description.
>
> You could write a full written response here if you want more practice, or you can use this page and the next one to create a full plan for the written response to the revision task. You may need to use an extra sheet of paper if writing a full response.

....
....
....
....
....
....
....
....
....
....
....
....
....
....
....
....
....
....
....
....
....

> Any written response in your actual assessment may have a word limit. Ask your tutor or check the Pearson website for the most up-to-date Sample Assessment Material and Mark Scheme to make sure you have the latest information.

Try to use correct **spelling** and **grammar** throughout your written response to convey a confident, professional approach.

....
....
....
....
....
....
....
....
....
....
....
....
....
....
....
....
....
....
....
....
....
....
....
....
....
....
....
....

Structuring your promotional portfolio

Before you start to create your promotional portfolio, it is important that you plan carefully what to include and check that this relates to the task information you have been given.

 In the space below, plan what you will include and how you will structure your promotional portfolio for the revision task. Make sure you:

- are clear about the requirements of the Heritage Theatre, and which of your skills are relevant to the opportunity (see your notes on pages 137–138)
- identify which pieces of evidence are most relevant and are in the best form to demonstrate your experience and skills match the project requirements
- provide relevant information about each piece of evidence, explaining why it is relevant and linking it to the employment opportunity and the workshop(s) you are proposing.

Planning your portfolio in this way will help to ensure your portfolio is clear and matches the brief you have been given.

....
....
....
....
....
....
....
....
....
....
....
....
....
....
....
....
....
....
....
....

The promotional portfolio: your CV

Use the space below to plan a CV in response to the revision task on page 133. Remember that your CV must give all the important information about you and should highlight relevant skills and experience for the employment opportunity.

....

....

....

....

....

....

....

....

....

....

....

....

....

....

....

....

....

....

....

....

....

....

....

....

Links To revise the information you could include in a CV, see page 163 of the Revision Guide.

The promotional portfolio: evidence

As part of your promotional portfolio, you will need to present evidence of your skills and experience including extracts of practical work. This could include audio and video clips, photographs, posters, certificates and testimonals, as well as your CV.

Remember to check with your tutor or look at the most up-to-date Sample Assessment Material on the Pearson website for details on how much evidence you can include (for example, how many minutes of video/audio or how many photos).

In this space, write down the details of the evidence you have decided to include, when it was created, and describe each piece of evidence. Make sure you build a portfolio that sends a clear and persuasive message with relevant examples that are consistent with your written response.

....

....

....

....

....

....

....

....

....

....

....

....

....

....

....

....

....

....

....

....

....

....

Answers

Unit 1: Investigating Practitioners' Work

These answers are in no way prescriptive and should be used for guidance only.

Page 4 Investigation process

Suggested answers could include the following.

Investigating contextual factors: historical, cultural, economic, political, technical, social, geographical, physical factors; influences from other practitioners and performers, teachers, education and mentors.

Relationship between contextual factors, creative intentions and themes: themes, genre, target audience, how practitioners' work has influenced others, collaborations, public and critical responses. Critical analysis of the work of performing arts practitioners: applying critical analysis skills (analyse, explore, interpret, prioritise, evaluate, make independent judgements, draw conclusions, links with other practitioners, possibility of further investigation). Present conclusions and independent judgements through effective investigation: summarising key information, and presenting findings and independent judgements.

Page 5 Primary research

1   Answers could include: conducting an interview, watching a live performance, conducting a survey, attending a pre- or after-show talk/discussion.
2   Your own response. This could be drawn from interviewing a teacher who works for a human rights organisation, for example, or a telephone interview with someone who works for a charity that is based around human rights. Information needs to be sourced effectively. Research findings will provide details about human rights, with examples.
3   Answers should include:
    · Advantages: the information is first-hand and thus is original.
    · Disadvantages: not always possible to attend performances/conduct interviews or discussions, depending on your locality as well as the financial implications.

Page 6 Secondary research

1   Web-based sources, print, archives, recorded/digital resources, case studies, key theories.
2   Your own response. Information needs to be sourced effectively.

Page 7 Collating information

1   **Boal:** the most relevant information is in points C, D and E.
    Bruce: the most relevant information is in points A, B and E.
    Stanislavski: the most relevant information is in points C, D and E.
2   Spider diagrams should include additional information gained from research.

Page 8 Documenting research sources

1   Title of work, year it was published, name of publisher, page number.
2   URL, paragraph number, date last accessed.
3   Yes.
4   Yes.
5   Footnotes are a way of organising quotations/citations. A number is placed after the quotation/citation, and the number then appears at the bottom of the page with the relevant source information.
6   · Organise it into different sections for books, websites, etc.
    · Put authors in alphabetical order.
    · Use an appropriate format and keep it consistent.

Page 9 Presentation of findings: referencing, citation and bibliography

1   A quotation is an exact copy of the words of an author, whereas a citation is used when you want to paraphrase or summarise an author's words.
2   Yes.
3   Yes.
4   For example:
    Dates when web pages were accessed should be included for all websites.
    Web pages should be listed.
    Books should be listed in alphabetical order.
    Paragraph numbers should be shown for all websites.
    Wikipedia should be avoided as a source because it is generally not accepted as an authoritative source.

Page 10 Historical and cultural contextual factors

1   Historical factors are factors that relate to key historical events and epochs, such as World War II.
2   Cultural factors are factors that relate to cultural background such as minority groups, world influences and communities.
3   Answers could include how **Boal** was influenced by epoch, in that he was very aware of social oppression at that point in history and thus created Theatre of Oppression to challenge social views and provide a better platform for the socially oppressed. Boal's theatrical methods almost try to change history in offering alternatives to historical occurrences (by allowing spectators to change the outcomes). Boal has been influenced culturally by other practitioners (Stanislavski and Brecht), as well as minority groups (the socially oppressed in Brazil) and world influences (poverty and oppression).
4   Suggested answers could include the following.

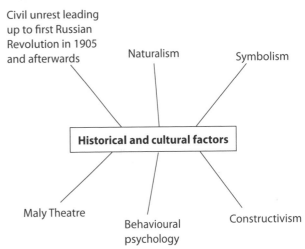

Civil unrest leading up to first Russian Revolution in 1905 and afterwards

Naturalism

Symbolism

Historical and cultural factors

Maly Theatre

Behavioural psychology

Constructivism

5   Your own response drawing on historical and cultural factors, providing more detail regarding some of the points made above.

Page 11 Economic and political contextual factors and practitioners' work

1   Economic factors are related to funding conditions and financial climate.
2   Political factors are related to legislation, propaganda, satire and current events.
3   Suggested answers could include the following.
    Boal:
    · Political situation forced him into exile in 1971.
    · He became a politician.
    · He wanted to promote the plight of the socially oppressed.

- He developed legislative theatre.
- He was influenced by Marxism.

Bruce:
- He integrated politics into dances in a brand new way.
- Pinochet's regime in Chile is reflected in *Ghost Dances*.
- Human rights/prisoner of conscience is reflected in *Swansong*.
- He was inspired by the work of Amnesty International.
- The death of Lorca by fascists in Spain is reflected in *Cruel Garden*.

Stanislavksi:
- He was under permanent surveillance, because his Moscow Art Theatre was frequently attended by dictators such as Joseph Stalin.
- He came from a rich background.
- He used his wealth to fund theatrical experiments.
- He was affected by political unrest (Russian Revolution).
- Performances mirrored political events such as Bloody Sunday.

Page 12 Technical and social contextual factors

1. Technical factors are related to the latest developments in technology as well as restrictions.
2. Social factors are related to fashion, values, media and audience expectation.
3. Answers could include how Boal was heavily influenced by values (he wanted to challenge social values), as well as audience expectations. Boal wanted the audience to become actively involved in the outcomes of the performance. Regarding technical factors, Boal did not place great importance on technical elements.
4. Suggested answers could include the following.

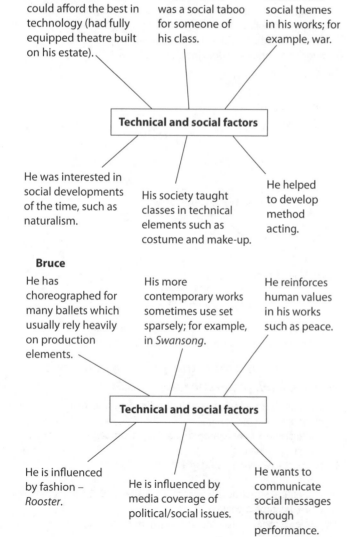

Stanislavski

His wealth meant he could afford the best in technology (had fully equipped theatre built on his estate).

To be an actor was a social taboo for someone of his class.

He mirrored social themes in his works; for example, war.

Technical and social factors

He was interested in social developments of the time, such as naturalism.

His society taught classes in technical elements such as costume and make-up.

He helped to develop method acting.

Bruce

He has choreographed for many ballets which usually rely heavily on production elements.

His more contemporary works sometimes use set sparsely; for example, in *Swansong*.

He reinforces human values in his works such as peace.

Technical and social factors

He is influenced by fashion – *Rooster*.

He is influenced by media coverage of political/social issues.

He wants to communicate social messages through performance.

5. Your own response drawing on technical and social factors, providing more detail regarding some of the points made in the spider diagram.

Page 13 Geographical and physical contextual factors

1. Geographical factors are related to venues.
2. Physical factors are related to the physical characteristics of a place.
3. Suggested answers could include the following.

Boal:
- Boal was influenced by being raised in Brazil.
- He tried to make classical drama more pertinent to Brazilian society.
- He wanted to perform in venues that were accessible to audiences (who could then participate in the performance).
- He was very much in touch with the environment (he was the Brazilian equivalent of a city councillor).
- His work is influenced by his political exile in Argentina.

Bruce:
- Most of his works would have been performed in conventional theatres.
- He choreographed for many ballet companies, so he would have needed to select a certain type of space (such as large venues).
- He uses the set to suggest geographical location (such as in *Ghost Dances*).
- He is influenced by issues in overseas locations.
- He is influenced by his upbringing and training in the UK, with a ballet bias.

Stanislavski:
- He was influenced by his upbringing in Russia.
- Due to his wealth, he had access to a range of theatres.
- He had his own theatre built on his estate.
- He used his wealth to open a society of art and literature, which had its own large stage.
- His family house became a focus for the artistic and cultural life of the city.

Page 14 Influences

1. If a practitioner is influenced by someone, it means that someone has had an effect on them.
2. Answers could include:
   Other practitioners and performers, education, teachers and mentors.
3. **Boal** was influenced by: Marxism, Brecht, Stanislavksi, Paulo Freire, doing a degree at Columbia University in USA, Arena Theatre.
   Bruce has been influenced by: the Rambert School, Amnesty International, Ballet Rambert, Marie Rambert, Glen Tetley, Norman Morrice.
4. **Stanislavksi** was influenced by: Alexander Pushkin, Nikolai Gogol, Mikhail Shchepkin, Leopold Tolstoy, Meiningen Ensemble, James–Lange psychophysiology.
5. **Boal** was influenced by: Marxist philosophies and also by the practitioners Brecht and Stanislavksi. Paulo Freire in particular had an influence on his work; he wrote a book 'Pedagogy of the Oppressed' which lead Boal to create 'Theatre of the Oppressed,' promoting social and political change. Boal would have been influenced by his studies in the USA to some extent; working at the Arena Theatre in Sao Paulo, he began to experiment with new forms of theatre.
   Bruce was influenced by: his training at the Rambert School which was mainly ballet training. He was influenced by the work of Amnesty International and went on to produce work which related to human rights. He was fortunate enough to be one of the last to be taught by Marie Rambert. Glen Tetley and Norman Morrice were choreographers who shared a similar background of academic and contemporary techniques.

Stanislavski was influenced by Pushkin, Gogol and Shchepkin at the Maly Theatre, where he worked. He was influenced by the work of Tolstoy, the Meiningen Ensemble (an important theatrical force in late nineteenth-century Germany). The James–Lange's theory of emotion also influenced Stanislavski's attention to realistic portrayal of feelings.

Page 15 Themes

1   Suggested answers could include the following:
    Boal: social themes such as oppression and isolation.
    Bruce: social themes such as political prisoners (*Swansong*) and Pinochet's coup (*Ghost Dances*).
    Stanislavski: the human predicament and social themes such as the effects of war.
2   Suggested answers could include the following:
    Boal communicates the theme of human rights by using interactive theatre (forum theatre), allowing spectators to influence the outcomes of the performance. He has also used legislative theatre where participants create bills that will address the oppression they face.
    Bruce communicates the theme of human rights by using different components such as movement, set, costume, music, lighting and props. For example, in *Swansong* the chairs add to the tension, the lighting creates the image of a cell, the music is electro-acoustic, interludes enable the audience to hear tapping of the feet, and movement is a mixture of tap and more classical styles.
    Stanislavksi communicates the theme of human rights through a method that is based on the concept of emotional memory. He used the 'magic if', which involves actors asking many questions of their characters and themselves. Stanislavski felt this could allow for more naturalistic performances.
3   Relating to Boal and Stanislavksi, answers could include their uniqueness in their methods of delivery (forum theatre and Stanislavski system). For Bruce, it is more to do with how he uses constituent features to create works that are fresh and exciting.

Page 16 Intentions, genre and target audiences

1   Genre means a style or category of performance.
2   The genre best used to describe the work of Boal is physical theatre. His work is not typical of the genre because it involved new methods such as forum theatre and legislative theatre. The genre best used to describe the work of Bruce is contemporary dance. His work is typical of some contemporary dance companies, where ballet is a main feature. The genre best used to describe the work of Stanislavski is realism. His work is not typical of the genre because it overlapped with naturalism, as he wanted to focus on the truth behind feeling and experience.
3   A target audience is a particular group at which a performance is aimed.
4   The target audience for Boal is the socially oppressed, minority groups.
    The target audience for Bruce is standard theatre audience, although he has broadened his target audience as he has included different styles of dance, such as tap, ballet and vaudeville.
    Stanislavksi believed that regardless of target audience, all performance should be of a high standard.
5   Your own response expanding on the above points. For example, you could write about how the audience interacts during Boal's performances and this empowers them as they are involved in making decisions.

Page 17 Influencing other people

1   **Boal:** influenced many artists in many ways with his participatory methods of expression; is viewed as the inspiration behind many twenty-first-century forms of

performance-activism; he set up a CTO (Centre for Theatre of the Oppressed) in Rio de Janeiro which would have been accessed by many people and thus influenced many.
    Bruce: there is little information on who Bruce has influenced, although his work has undoubtedly inspired and influenced many people.
    Stanislavksi: influenced Boal in that they shared the view that personal memories and experiences are stimuli for drama; influenced Boleslavsky and Ouspenskaya (his former students) who founded the American Laboratory Theatre; The Group Theatre (Strasberg, Clurman, Crawford) put Stanislavski's initial discoveries into practice.
2   Your own response expanding on the points above/adding more information. For example, you could write about Stanislavski's innovative contribution to naturalism, which has remained at the core of mainstream Western performance training for most of the last hundred years.

Page 18 Collaborations

1   Collaboration means working together to realise shared goals.
2   Other practitioners, set designers, musicians, costume designers, lighting designers.
3   **Bruce:** *Cruel Garden* collaboration with Lindsay Kemp; Bruce was choreographer and Kemp directed and designed costumes. Collaborated with designers Nadine Baylis and John B Reed, also collaborated with Philip Chambon (performer, producer and composer) in the creation of *Nature Dances* for Houston Ballet. Also associated with Dutch painter Walter Nobbe, Pamela Marre (storyteller) and his wife Marian Bruce (designer/sculptor).
    Boal: Arena Theatre, collaborated with the community with his interactive performances. Collaborated with Paulo Freire to develop educational and artistic methods. Collaborated with prisoners in Rio and São Paulo and with his son Julian.
    Stanislavski: collaborated with the writers Tolstoy and Anton Chekhov, with the theatre practitioner Edward Gordon Craig and the director Vsevolod Meyerhold.
4   Your own response, expanding on the points above/adding additional information and providing further detail.

Page 19 Public and critical responses

1   Responses from the public and/or critics, in the form of reviews or comments in, for example, newspapers, blogs or tweets. These can be positive or negative or a combination of both. They can contribute to shaping public opinions as well as having a potential impact on future work or indeed on funding prospects for future projects.
2   Practitioners may choose to take on board the opinions of the audience/critic, or they can ignore them.
3   Public and critical responses to Boal's work include being received positively by some, although he challenged conventions and was forced into exile by the Brazilian government. This affected his work by creating the interactive relationship with the audience, which meant that the audience really engaged with the performance and the work became more accessible.
    Public and critical responses to Bruce's work include a positive reception, although he too has had his critics. He took critical responses on board and made contemporary dance more accessible by introducing other dance styles.
    Public and critical responses to Stanislavski's work include mostly positive reviews, although he did have critics. This affected his work by creating difficulties for those who worked with him. For example, Brecht found his methods too restrictive at times, which led him to change the focus of performances with the emphasis being on the social message rather than the characters.

Page 20 Performance styles: repertoire

1   Repertoire is a body of items that are performed regularly.
2   It is significant because it can provide insight regarding the characteristics of a practitioner; it is used to communicate meaning.

3

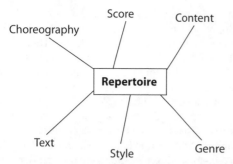

Repertoire
- Choreography
- Score
- Content
- Text
- Style
- Genre

4 **Boal:** Repertoire in relation to the practitioner is significant because it was unique in that it was flexible, relating to events and issues at the time; it was a process rather than a set repertoire. It highlighted social injustice. Repertoire is used by the practitioner to communicate meaning by the interactive nature of performances. The style/genre of the repertoire is forum theatre, although some work such as legislative theatre is not typical of the style/genre.

Bruce: Repertoire in relation to the practitioner is significant because it voiced social and political messages. Repertoire is used by the practitioner to communicate meaning by using the constituent features of dance. The style/genre of the repertoire is naturalism, although it also embraces elements of realism.

Stanislavski: Repertoire in relation to the practitioner is significant because it reflected the new techniques which he had created based on emotional expression. Repertoire is used by the practitioner to communicate meaning by addressing social themes such as the effects of war. The style/genre of the repertoire is questionable as it embraces elements of both naturalism and realism; however, it is linked more to realism.

5 Your own response, using key words for any of the practitioners based on the information above.

Page 21 Performance styles: performance

Answers could include some of the following key points:

Boal believed in the importance of movement (he placed emphasis on exercise). He believed that human relationships are structured in a theatrical way, including our use of voice modulation, body language and use of space.

Bruce used music to enhance his performances; musical score was significant when choreographing for ballet works. He also used popular music to set the scene such as in *Rooster*. His use of gesture in *Rooster* (mimicking chickens) was highly effective!

Stanislavksi focused on character in the expression of emotion. He used a combination of these elements to provide realistic performances.

Page 22 Performance styles: relationships

1 Performer to audience, contact work, performer to space, performer to performer, performer to accompaniment, placement and role of audience.

2 Performer to performer – The relationship that performers have with each other on stage.
Contact work – Contact between performers such as lifts, falls, physical combat.
Performer to space – How a performer uses the space such as pathways and levels.
Performer to audience – Is the purpose to entertain the audience, or to alienate or challenge them?
Performer to accompaniment – Performers may react to sound effects or dance/sing in time to music.
Placement and role of audience – Where the audience are situated as well as whether they might interact with the performance, for example.

3 Relationships between musical accompaniment and dance are demonstrated in the work of Bruce; for example, in *Swansong* he demonstrates the interrogation through the tapping noises of the prisoners' and guards' feet, as well as clicks and claps to heighten the tension. Bruce also uses bird noises to convey the feeling of being trapped in a cell (like a bird in a cage).

Other relationships that relate to his work are all those listed for answer 1. These are significant because they are all used to communicate meaning. For example, contact work is used to demonstrate struggle in *Swansong*. The audience are there to be entertained but also to learn about social and political issues. Stanislavski wanted his performer/audience relationship to be close, drawing the audience in through emotionally charged performances that draw on the actors' experiences and memories. Other relationships that relate to his work are all those listed for answer 1. These are significant because he wanted to develop relationships between the cast rather than focusing on individual parts. He encouraged his actors to imagine different types of realities between audiences and performers.

Page 23 Performance styles: production, design and technical

1 Your own response.
Answers to questions 2 and 3 could include some of the following key points:
- **Set: Bruce** used set to suggest an environment; for example, in *Ghost Dances* where the painted backdrop represents a rocky plain and cave opening. **Boal** did not place significance on set in his works, but used it if it was available. **Stanislavski** wanted to create realistic sets; for example, in *The Lower Depths* he uses photographs to recreate the interior of the house. He also uses set to add to the dramatic action; for example, where he litters what was a tidy room with children's toys in *Three Sisters*.
- **Costume: Bruce** used costume to emphasise character or enhance mood; for example, in *Ghost Dances* the ghosts wear wigs and rags and have skull-like masks and bodies painted to suggest bones and muscles. **Boal** did not use costumes unless they were available. **Stanislavksi** made sure that costumes were produced to be accurate for the production, rather than using old costumes from the company or pieces of the actor's own clothing.
- **Make-up: Bruce** used make-up in *Ghost Dances*; the 'Dead' wear stylised make-up that emphasises their eyes. **Boal** did not use make-up unless it was available. Stanislavski used make-up to help create realistic characters.
- **Mask: Bruce** used masks for the ghost in *Ghost Dances* to reinforce character. **Boal** only used production elements if they were available. **Stanislavski's** focus was on expression (much of which can be communicated through the face); thus masks were not a popular feature of his work.
- **Lighting: Bruce** used lighting in *Swansong* to help depict the image of the prisoner living in a cell; a diagonal shaft of light appears as if from a small window. **Boal** again only used lighting if it was available. **Stanislavski** insisted that natural-looking lighting should be achieved on stage, and tried to mask stage lights for a more realistic portrayal.
- **Sound: Bruce** used sound to heighten tension in *Swansong* where the guards and prisoners tap out an interrogation. For **Boal** sound is not an integral part of the performance; however, he does use rhythms in his warm-up games. **Stanislavski** placed importance on sound in performance; he had links with opera and used music to help create a realistic setting.
- **Special effects: Bruce** and **Boal** were not reliant on special effects for their performances. **Stanislavski** would use them if they made the performance more realistic.
- **Puppetry:** None of the three practitioners used puppetry significantly.
- **Multimedia:** None of the three practitioners used multimedia significantly.

Human rights: **Bruce** used costume, set, music, lighting and make-up to help communicate human rights themes. **Boal** did not place any emphasis on production elements; instead he used the 'spect-actors' themselves to re-enact live events. **Stanislavski** was interested in using production elements to communicate social issues; however, his focus was more on the 'human condition' and emotional truth.

Page 24 Summarise key information

1 Unreliable sources may provide unreliable information. For example, Wikipedia may sometimes include false or mistaken information, as anyone can edit an article on the site.
2 For example:

Piece	Boal: Theatre of the Oppressed	Bruce: Swansong	Stanislavski: The Three Sisters
Repertoire	It is typical of his desire to address the plight of the socially oppressed, based on theatrical techniques which engage and involve the audience.	Popular piece of repertoire, typical of his repertoire in communicating a strong social/political message.	Directed and performed in plays, although was more well-known for developing the 'Stanislavski System' (relating to acting techniques) which he applied to productions directed by him.
Performance	Uses movement and dialogue to communicate meaning.	Movement, gesture and character all significant in communicating the theme (e.g. recurring motifs which are developed throughout). Musicality and timing are essential for example in the tap sections. Dynamic variations help to create tension, for example in the trio section.	He used a combination of performance elements to communicate a realistic expression of emotion, wanting the performers to fully immerse themselves in their characters. In *The Three Sisters* as with other works, he tried to make the characters real by applying his techniques such as the 'magic if'.
Relationships	Significant, especially between performer and audience, in that the audience interacts with the performers and can alter the course of action. Relationship between the performers is important as it communicates meaning to the audience.	Significant throughout. Between performer and audience tension is created, as well as making the audience address uncomfortable issues. Between performers, the main relationship is between the prisoner and guards. Contact work is used to help establish this relationship.	The theme is accessible to the audience, as it is about the clash between the ambitions and dreams of youth which are constricted by the realities of life. Relationships between performers help to reveal the themes, through interactions between characters.
Production, design and technical elements	Boal did not place importance on these elements.	Props, set, costume, lighting and sound all contribute significantly. He uses the chair to help build tension, the bare set and carefully plotted lighting to suggest the cell space, costumes to establish character and the tapping and bird noises to help further the plot and create an atmosphere.	He used these elements to create more realistic performances; for example when he uses props (children's toys) strewn across the room to signify the presence of children.

Page 25 Analyse and explore

1 'Analyse' means to examine something methodically and in detail.
2 'Explore' means to investigate.
3 Suggested answers could include the following.
   Boal: Geographical factor – affected by his political exile in Argentina.
   Social factor – wanted to challenge social views.
   Historical factor – tried to change the course of history through forum theatre.
   Bruce: Social factor – wanted to communicate strong social messages.
   Geographical factor – influenced by situations overseas.
   Political factor – created material that integrated political themes.
   Stanislavski: Historical factor – civil unrest prior to and following the Russian Revolution.
   Social factor – included social themes such as war.
   Economic factor – his wealth and privileged background enabled him to access a range of theatres.
4 **Boal:** lively, dynamic, resolute, militant.
   Bruce: timeless themes, musical dances (*Rooster*); steps communicate meaning.
   Stanislavksi: extremely influential; improved Checkhov's *The Seagull*; own company rejected his theories.
5 Your own response, expanding on the points above in relation to one of the selected practitioners and providing further detail.

Page 26 Interpreting and prioritising information

1 'Interpret' means to explain the meaning of something.
2 'Prioritise' means to designate something as being the most important or urgent.
3 **Boal:** forum theatre, legislative theatre, interactive with audience, challenged political and social views, audience become 'spect-actors'.
   Bruce: Strong social messages, integrated political themes, Amnesty International, other styles of dance, classical ballet training.
   Stanislavski: personal memories and experiences, different to Brecht's method acting, family's wealth, the 'magic if', techniques of emotional expression.
4 In terms of prioritising: for **Boal** forum theatre and challenging social/political views; for **Bruce,** strong social messages and integration of political themes; for **Stanislavski** drawing on personal memories, experiences, and techniques for emotional expression.
5 Answers should cover the significance of the information, the impact on the practitioners' work as well as how it relates to the theme.

Page 27 Evaluating and making independent judgements

1 'Evaluate' means to assess.
2 'Make independent judgements' means to formulate your own opinions.
3 **Boal's** strengths: fought for human rights; allowed performance to be more accessible to wider audiences; allowed his audience to interact with performances; enabled his audience to write bills (legislative theatre).
   Boal's weaknesses: his work sometimes lacked credibility as he was a middle-class white man working on behalf of the socially oppressed to improve human rights; some found his views to be controversial; some thought his techniques were weak.
   Bruce's strengths: broadened his audience by including different dance styles; communicates strong social and political messages raising awareness of human rights; able to combine constituent features to create successful dance works; successful as both a performer and choreographer.
   Bruce's weaknesses: there is little information on this subject, although it does not necessarily mean that Bruce had no weaknesses!
   Stanislavski's strengths: made acting more accessible by tapping into real emotions; created pieces based on social messages; developed techniques that have stood the test of time; created exciting theatre; raised the standards of theatre which were poor at the time.
   Stanislavski's weaknesses: his techniques may have inefficiencies; his techniques should not be used in isolation but in conjunction with other techniques.
4 Your own response in relation to one practitioner; personal opinions should be provided in bullet points in the spider diagram.

Page 28 Conclusions, links and further investigation 1

1 **Boal**

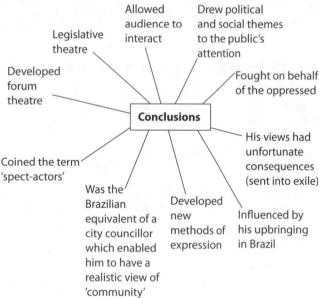

Bruce

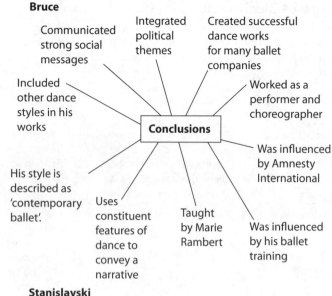

Stanislavski

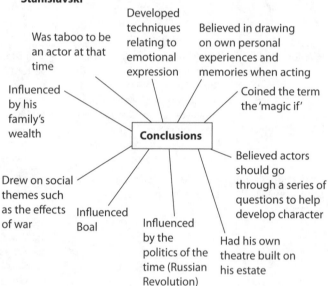

2 Examples of similarities:
   Bruce – was influenced by Marie Rambert, collaborated with Philip Chambon, shared a similar background to choreographers Glen Tetley and Norman Morrice.
   Boal – was influenced by and had similar creative intentions to Stanislavski, collaborated with Paulo Freire, believed (like Brecht) that theatre was a powerful tool in bringing about social change.
   Stanislavski – influenced Boal, collaborated with Tolstoy and Chekhov, was influenced by Pushkin and Gogol, was similar to Brecht in that they developed their own systems of acting and rejected the idea of stars in a performance.

Page 29 Conclusions, links and further investigation 2

1 Your own response exploring similarities; **how** and **why** they are connected. For example, Boal and Stanislavski shared the intention of showing realistic expression of emotion (the different ways that they achieved this could then be elaborated upon).
2 Suggesting how relationships between practitioners could be investigated further will demonstrate that a deeper understanding can be gained if required.

Page 30 Presentation of findings: format, structure and tone

1 I will need to plan the structure of my written work, so that it is accessible and easy to navigate. I could try to plan what will be in each paragraph so that it will make it easier for me to cover all the required elements of the essay. I will need to start off with an introduction in which I will state what I will be covering in the essay. I will also need to end with a conclusion, which will summarise my information.

2 For example:
According to research sources …
I have come to the conclusion that …
Firstly, I intend to outline my main areas of investigation …
Although some critics believe that … I am of the opinion that …
Regarding contextual factors, I believe that …
My first choice of practitioner is …
Relationships between performers are particularly significant in the work of …

Page 31 Presentation of findings: language and subject-specific terminology

1 The most appropriate sentences are:
I believe that Boal's use of political themes is effective because …
Bruce's work is highly successful due to several factors …
Stanislavski was original in his use of …
These sentences are appropriate because they are specific and use more sophisticated language than the others

2 For example:

Dance	Acting	Musical theatre
Choreography	Dialogue	Pitch
Dynamic range	Character	Vocal range
Motif development	Projection	Modulation
Coordination	Physicality	Intonation
Alignment	Stage presence	Score
Elevation	Body language	Libretto
Marking	Blocking	Orchestra

3 Your own response, including relevant terminology.

Page 32 Presenting structured arguments

1 Answers could include the following:
   - Consider the positive and negative points of what you have said, as well as how reliable it is.
   - Think about their relevance to the debate, and how they can be incorporated into the argument.
   - Don't force ideas; believe in what you are writing.

2 The text launches straight in without an introduction; it is disjointed; there is no evidence to back up the points.

3 Stanislavski's methods were influenced by previous practitioners such as the Meiningen Company and their radical production style.
Bruce choreographed work for many ballet companies such as Houston Ballet and English National Ballet.
Boal developed several theatre techniques such as forum theatre and legislative theatre.

Pages 33–38 Your own response

Your own response.

Unit 3: Group Performance Workshop

These answers are in no way prescriptive and should be used for guidance only.

Page 41 Planning and interpretation of stimulus

1 Examples could include cold, wet, tired, lonely, desperate, need, ill, pain.

2 Your own response.

3 For example, 'I researched homelessness as a starting point' or 'I improvised around the feeling of hunger and how it affects the way you move'.

Page 42 Research

Your own response.

Page 43 Form and style of performance

1 Your own response.

2 Your own response; partial example answer provided.

3 You will need to consider personal challenges such as maintaining vocal control while delivering emotional content, or communicating the theme effectively through the medium of contemporary dance. Suggestions on how to overcome difficulties could include specific exercises relating to vocal control or the use of gestures, dialogue or production elements to help communicate meaning.

Page 44 Artistic intention and target audience

1 Your own response, considering that artistic intention relates to the purpose or meaning of what you to communicate.

2 Examples could include movement, dance, songs, costume, set, props, music.

3 Your own response. Remember that a target audience is a particular group at which a performance is aimed; for example, school children could be the target audience for a TIE performance.

4 Examples could include age, gender, race, cultural background, socio-economic background.

Page 45 Creative/staging possibilities

1 Your own response. Answers should include consideration of how much space is required, where the audience will be seated and whether set will be used.

2 Having selected the appropriate performance pathway, you should provide examples of strengths and weaknesses such as projection, vocal skills, use of gesture, stamina, strength, control, facial expression, musicality and so on.

3 Specific examples should be provided such as, 'I will exercise for 20 minutes a day to help build up my stamina' or, 'I will practise pulling faces in front of a mirror to extend my range of facial expressions'.

Page 46 Development of creative ideas

1 Answers could include the following: maintaining technique, contact, staying 'in the moment', use of pause, continuity, originality.

2 Consider exercises such as improvisational tasks, 'word a minute', hot-seating.

3 Answers could include recording on video, audio recording, taking photographs, using diagrams.

4 Answers will need to include the practitioner and their technique/method such as Stanislavski – method acting; Merce Cunningham – chance method.

Page 47 Technical elements

1 Your own response.
2 Answers could include reference to where the audience are in relation to the performers, projection/exaggeration of voice, movement or facial expression.

Page 48 Structure

1 Examples could be included such as canon, unison, inversion, embellishment, instrumentation and so on.
2 Structure is literally a way of structuring movement. Other examples could include ternary, rondo, chance, theme and variation, narrative.
3 Your own response.

Page 49 Developing and shaping material

1 Answers could include:
   (a) Reasons such as some material not being as relevant to the intention or of inferior quality and therefore can be discarded. Selecting the most relevant and appropriate material will help to ensure a more successful performance. Also, too much material may have been produced, thus some will have to be discarded.
   (b) Feedback from peers could provide valuable information regarding material and how effective it is in communicating intention. Taking on board other people's ideas provides a broader perspective. Responding to and absorbing comments from others could help to enhance performance material.
   (c) Shaping and refining material allows adjustments to take place, such as making alterations about spacing, content or communication of intention. Whether they are major or minor alterations, performance material can be improved through this process.

Page 50 Explaining and justifying your creative decisions

For example:
1 Explanation: I made a decision to address how the space was being used. This meant going through each scene and seeing if the space had been used effectively, for example checking levels, directions and pathways, as well as whether we had used the stage space to maximum effect.
2 Justification: I think this was a valuable decision, as our performance tended to cover one part of the stage rather than maximising the space we had. Going through each scene enabled us to make the necessary adjustments about space such as adding the chairs, which provided extra dimensions to explore.

Page 51 Personal management and rehearsal skills

1 Suggested answers could include:
   - Attendance – builds self-discipline; prepares you for the professional world; poor attendance could impact on casting of roles; could impact on achievement. Examples will be your own.
   - Punctuality – builds self-discipline; prepares you for the professional world; poor punctuality could mean that warm-ups/rehearsals/vital information is missed; could impact on achievement.
   - Meeting deadlines – instils self-discipline; prepares you for the professional world; could impact on your and others' achievement. Examples will be your own.
2 Examples could include: copying tutor/peers; reading through scripts and scores; practising repeatedly; listening to /watching back material; writing notes; rehearsing with and without prompts; practising in front of a small audience; breaking down movement phrases.

Page 52 Team skills

Answers could include the following. Examples will be your own.
- Taking direction – could enhance performance material; shows a willingness to take on board feedback; could be important, for example relating to health and safety; adds another perspective/opinion.
- Giving direction – demonstrates decision-making and leadership skills; shows confidence; could enhance performance material.
- Trust and cooperation – trust will enable you to feel comfortable and confident when performing, as well as taking risks and trusting each other doing catches, lifts and, falls. Cooperation will enable you to work in a team effectively, to avoid injury, to work collectively towards a main objective and to achieve better results.
- Contributing ideas – could enhance performance material; shows independent thinking and creativity; demonstrates decision-making; personal contribution can make you feel 'ownership' of the piece.
- Receptiveness and responsiveness to the ideas of others – breeds positivity and equality; allows you to feel safe to voice ideas; enhances the creative environment and potentially the quality of the performance material.

Page 53 Review and reflect

1 Review means to evaluate, and reflect means to think deeply about something.
2 They are important because through review and reflection, performance material can be enhanced, for example addressing areas for improvement.
3 Both the process and performance.
4 You will consider audience feedback.
5 The areas that might be considered are possible professional lighting, staging, technical elements such as rigging, more advanced costume, make-up or specialist footwear. Relevant examples will be dependent on your own performance.
6 Answers could include: interpretation of stimulus and ideas; use of exploratory techniques; development of performance skills; strengths (process and performance); areas for improvement (process and performance); effectiveness of own performance skills; effectiveness of the performance in terms of intention; development of material and performance skills if this were to be a professional production.

Page 54 Strengths and areas for improvement

Answers should relate to physical, interpretive, vocal, music, performance skills.
For example:
Strength – Stamina: this is sustained physical/vocal effort; I have built up effective stamina through increased levels of physical activity such as daily exercise including dance classes and running. This enables me to perform with good energy levels on stage, for the duration of a performance.
Area for improvement – Pitch: this means how high or low a note is; I could improve on my pitch particularly the higher notes, by doing breathing exercises and singing scales for example.

Pages 55–59 Reviewing

You can practise skills audits, which could feed into the digital process log entry based on the set task provided. The audits will help you to focus on direct, short answers relating to each milestone, which could then be expanded.

Page 55 Reviewing the creative process

Example of expanded response

Interpretation of stimulus and ideas – rating 3
Our intention was fairly clear, and we managed to communicate the theme of poverty through the medium of musical theatre. To make it clearer I would have developed the sections of text between songs and dances to make the plot more apparent. Although the lyrics of the songs did relate to the plot, they perhaps did not convey the plot as effectively as dialogue could have done. This is because the combination of music and lyrics along with the dances would have engaged the audience effectively but not stated the plot clearly, as it was a bit complex. Therefore, we could also look at making the plot a bit simpler if we were to do this project again.

Own development and contribution of ideas – rating 3
I input ideas at points, such as developing the idea of hunger in relation to mime through the use of gesture. This then fed well into the performance as one section was purely mime, which I enjoyed developing through physicality and facial expression. However, I feel that I could have contributed more effectively in the early stages when we were considering what structure the piece would take and what form/styles would be incorporated. I tended to leave the decisions at this point up to other members of the group. I could have improved this by being more proactive during the creative process, providing more ideas and getting more involved right from the start.

Page 56 Reviewing the rehearsal process

Example of expanded response

Participation in group tasks – rating 5
I consider that I participated extremely well in all group tasks. I sometimes lead warm-ups and cool downs and always join in with the activities with full energy and commitment. During creative group tasks that we set ourselves, I consistently participated with enthusiasm and concentration. When developing material, I remained alert and responsive throughout.

Page 57 Reviewing skills

Example of expanded response

Tone, pace and timing of delivery – rating 1
I struggled to deliver my lines effectively as I kept rushing them, which meant that I was not heard properly. This had an impact on other performers, as it affected when they delivered their lines because they couldn't hear me properly. Also I had the audience to consider. I worked on this by practising breathing exercises. These helped me to relax, which had a knock-on effect on the pace of my lines.

Balance, alignment and posture – rating 2
I found it difficult to maintain my alignment when performing. I had already struggled with this in rehearsal; when I watched myself in the mirror I could see that my fingers were spiky and also that my arms were raised too high (rather than being at shoulder height). As I was trying to focus on remembering the movements I kept forgetting about my alignment. I could improve my alignment by knowing the material better so that I don't have to concentrate on remembering it. This would enable me to focus on correcting my alignment. I could also use mirrors to help me correct my alignment and/or watch myself back on video.

Page 58 Reviewing the effectiveness of your performance

Example of expanded response

Was the intention clear? – rating 3
Our intention was fairly clear, and we managed to communicate the theme of poverty through the medium of musical theatre. To make it clearer I would have developed the sections of text between songs and dances to make the plot more apparent. Although the lyrics of the songs did relate to the plot, they perhaps did not convey the plot as effectively as dialogue could have done. This is because the combination of music and lyrics along with the dances would have engaged the audience effectively but not stated the plot clearly, as it was a bit complex. Therefore we could also have looked at making the plot a bit simpler if we were to do this project again.

Page 59 Assessing audience reaction and possible future development

Example of expanded response

Development of the material (audience feedback) – rating 4
The majority of the audience thought that costume, props and light were successful, and also that the intention was clear. Only a few audience members thought that the message could have been clearer, as they didn't understand the meaning of the dances. Some commented that the costumes distracted from the movement, and that the lighting was too dark to read facial expression effectively. These comments could be taken on board by making the dances more accessible and perhaps reconsidering the motifs to make them clearer. Regarding costume and lighting, the costumes could be simpler and the lighting could be brighter to counteract the issues.

Pages 60–63 Planning and interpretation of stimulus

Practise Milestone 1 entry based on the set task provided. This focuses on the preparation and planning stages. Examples will need to be provided, with the emphasis on individual contribution. Answers should cover interpretation of stimulus, planning and generation of ideas. Consider: the form and style of the performance; the target audience; how to communicate creative intention; applying practical performance skills; time and resources available.

Pages 64–66 Development of creative ideas (early stage review)

Practise Milestone 2 entry based on the set task provided. This focuses on development of creative ideas. Examples will need to be provided, with the emphasis on individual contribution. Answers should cover participation in practical activities to shape and develop the material; experimentation with forms and styles; applying performance skills to communicate the group's creative intentions. Consider exploratory techniques; ideas for form and content; selection and development of performance skills; personal management and collaborative skills; the duration of the piece.

Pages 67–69 Development of creative ideas (mid-stage review)

Practise Milestone 3 entry based on the set task provided. This focuses on the mid-stage of the creative process. Examples will need to be provided, with the emphasis on individual contribution. Answers should cover participation in practical activities to shape and develop the material; experimentation with forms and styles; applying performance skills to communicate the group's creative intention. Consider exploratory techniques; ideas for form and content; selection and development of performance skills; personal managements and collaborative skills; the duration of the piece.

Pages 70–72 Review and reflection

Practise Milestone 4 entry based on the set task provided. This focuses on reviewing and reflecting on the process and performance. Examples will need to be provided, with the emphasis on individual contribution; however, the impact of others' ideas can also be commented on. Answers should cover personal strengths and weaknesses, and how the piece could be developed as a fully resourced professional production. Consider personal management and collaborative skills; the impact of your own contribution and that of others; ideas for further development of the performance; feedback and response from your invited audience.

Unit 5: Individual Performance Commission

These answers are in no way prescriptive and should be used for guidance only.

Page 76 Studying your commission brief

1. (a) Type of commissioning body: museum.
   (b) Purpose of commissioning body: to promote the launch of its new building
   (c) Objective of the commission: to inform the public about the launch of the new building; to promote science in education; to provide entertaining and stimulating performances.
   (d) Target audience: teenagers.
   (e) Length of performance: five to eight minutes.
   (f) Logistics: considerations such as production elements and the fact that it is a solo performance.

Page 77 The purpose of the commission

1. The purpose(s) of the commissioning body are to inform the public about the launch of the new building and also to promote science in education; to provide entertaining and stimulating performances.
2. The purpose is to be educational and informative – conveying information about the new building and the importance of science in education will need to be considered.
3. Answers could include: science, robot, entertain, new building, futuristic, fun, outer space, gadgets.

Page 78 Target audience

1. A target audience is a particular group at which a performance is aimed.
2.

Age — Gender

Target audience

Religious/cultural beliefs — Socio-economic background

3. Your own response considering the four points above.
4. Your own response relating to whether the performance was a success.

Page 79 Needs of the target audience

1. The target audience type is teenagers and the age range is 13–19. The gender of the target audience is male and female.
2. Answers could include suggestions such as:
   Because the target audience type is teenagers, I will need to ensure that I consider their interests and educational level. Regarding age, I will need to create material that uses appropriate language and current trends such as music and social media. The gender of the target audience will mean that my performance material will need to appeal equally to males and females. Gender will not really affect the decisions made. Science, however, is often not as appealing to females as to males, so consideration of how it could be more accessible for females would be valuable.
3. Social and cultural issues may occur. For example, the perception of science can be 'geeky' which is social stigma. This could be overcome by making it more accessible through the use of popular music, links with social media, incorporating 'buzz' words and taking on board current trends. Cultural issues could occur such as some topics/music/performance styles/costumes not being viewed as appropriate. Cultural diversity would need to be considered.

Page 80 The context of the brief

1. Context in relation to a commission brief means the circumstances that form the setting for the commission.

2. The objectives of the commission brief are to inform the public about the launch of the new building, to promote science in education, and to provide entertaining and stimulating performances.
3. Monologue, songs, movement, dance, mime, a combination of these elements.
4. The commissioning body is a museum, therefore I will need to ensure that I consider the credibility of the museum and respect the vision of the museum and its exhibits.
   The commissioning body's requirements might be different from those of other commissioning bodies because the museum is not trying to sell anything or raise money, it is trying to promote and inform.
5. There is no specific reference to the past or future events in the commission brief. However, the brief is forward looking in terms of promoting science and the 'launch' event. The commission brief is clearly intended to have a long-lasting impact on its target audience, who will hopefully revisit the museum and renew/discover an interest in science following the reopening.

Page 81 Requirements and constraints

1. Your choice of stimulus.
2. Answers should include considerations of the visual and media stimuli such as conveying the sophistication of Hubo the Robot, and putting across quite a complex discovery about the ninth planet.
3. Both stimuli work effectively with the commission brief, as they link to science and would be of interest to teenagers as they are futuristic and exciting. Constraints may include not being predictable in conveying the 'robot' theme. Also, communicating an outer space theme would need to be unpredictable (avoid using slow motion) and approached with originality.
4. Suggested answers could include making schedules, planning the creative process carefully, being disciplined in meetings, setting deadlines, setting alarms, being organised and efficient.

Page 82 Response to the stimulus

1. Stimulus 1 – words such as planet, galaxy, earth, Neptune, star, orbit, darkness, moon, sun, alien, space.
   Stimulus 2 – words such as robot, robotic, grab, wave, futuristic, mechanical, metal, slick, gadget, human-like.
2. Your own response to the selected words.
3. For example, for Stimulus 2 the six starting points could be:
   - Think of an alternative way of moving like a robot which is new and original, based on dynamic variation.
   - Use robot 'speak' as a starting point for creating a monologue.
   - Use sound effects related to robots to create a soundscape.
   - Write lyrics for a song based on the daily life of a robot.
   - Improvise around the idea of a robot performing daily tasks.
   - Create a monologue from the robot's point of view about life among humans.

Page 83 Research

Your own responses. References should be sourced effectively.

Page 84 Practical exploration of stimulus

1. Answers could include: being spontaneous, maintaining technique, use of pause, use of contact, being 'in the moment', taking risks.
2. Improvisation means not practised or planned; spontaneous. It is useful when creating material as it enables performers to be experimental and explore stimuli. Ideas then start to flow. It is important to try to 'think outside the box', which means not choosing the most obvious ideas, but going beyond that. Other practical tasks that can help create material are try-outs, hot-seating and other creative tasks. Using feedback from my peers enables me to evaluate my improvisations; I can then select and refine the best material.

Page 85 Developing material from your stimulus

1. Your own responses in relation to creative ideas linked to Stimulus 1 or 2 and the commission brief.
2. Selection of material is important when creating performance material, as I need to identify the best bits that clearly communicate the purpose of the performance.
3. Rejection of material is also important because otherwise too much material may be generated, or it may not all be relevant or interesting.
4. In order to make this process easier, I make sure that I document the creative process by recording creative tasks, writing notes, recording peer feedback.

Pages 86–87 Responding to the commission brief

1. Your own response relating to a teenage audience. For example, use of appropriate language, including reference to current trends, popular music and dance/theatrical styles.
2. Your own response relating to structure. For example, performance of one continuous solo (which could be punctuated by transitions, use of different performance styles or musical interludes) or performance of a series of short solos.
3. Your own response relating to informing and educating. For example, use of structure, form, production elements, physical, vocal, music and performance skills to communicate meaning.
4. Your own response relating to entertainment and stimulation. For example, use of structure, form, production elements, physical, vocal, music and performance skills to provide entertainment and stimulation.
5. Your own response relating to costume. For example, to create a visual effect, enhance the mood, establish a character.
6. Your own response in relation to set and lighting. For example, to highlight the performance, create a mood, establish a location, setting or period in time.
7. Your own response in relation to music/sound. For example, to create a mood; establish a setting, location or period in time; develop the plot; provide a rhythm/beat.
8. Your own response in relation to performance pathway, including positive ways in which the performance pathway lends itself to solo performance.

Pages 88–89 Recording your stimulus responses

1. Your own response describing the reasons for selection of stimulus.
2. Your own response in relation to primary and secondary research and what insight this has provided.
3. Your own response to creative tasks. For example, improvisation.
4. Your own response in relation to the teenage audience. For example, technology, futurism, gadgets, the unknown.
5. Your own response in relation to your material and its links to the commission brief. For example, both relate to science and education.
6. Your own response in connection with your choice of stimulus. For example, informing about the launch of the new building and educating about science through monologue, dance, movement, songs.
7. Your own response in relation to structure. For example, one long solo/a series of short solos, use of choreographic or musical structures such as AB.
8. Your own response in relation to style and communication of meaning. For example, dance/theatrical/musical theatre styles such as contemporary dance, forum theatre, jukebox musical. You should include reasons for your choices.
9. Your own response in relation to performance skills. For example, projection, focus, musicality. Examples of physical, vocal, music skills such as stamina/flexibility, diction/characterisation, pitch/modulation.

Page 90 Application of performance skills to meet the commission brief

1. Answers could include: projection, facial expression, control, stage presence, communication of meaning, musicality, use of dynamics, phrasing, vocalisation, timing, emphasis.
2. Your choice of five performance skills.
3. Your own reasons for selection. For example, musicality could be important as you will be dancing to music as well as singing songs; or timing could be important as you are performing a monologue which requires comic timing.
4. Your own response. For example, doing regular breathing exercises to improve vocal range, or undertaking regular stretching exercises to improve flexibility.

Page 91 Communication of creative intentions

1. Answers should include reference to informing the public about the launch of the new building, promoting science in education, providing entertaining and stimulating performances.
2. Answers should include reference to science and education.
3. Answers could include suggestions such as asking for peer feedback, watching back recordings of rehearsals/development of material, making a checklist of objectives to refer back to.

Page 92 Structure

Your own responses, considering the performance being developed in response to the commission brief.

Page 93 Use of space

Your own responses, considering the performance being developed in response to the commission brief.

Page 94 Use of props, set and costume

Your own responses, considering the performance being developed in response to the commission brief.

Page 95 Use of sound and light

Your own responses, considering the performance being developed in response to the commission brief.

Page 96 Use of performance skills

Your own responses, considering the performance being developed in response to the commission brief.
Your own written evaluation.

Page 97 Evaluating effectiveness of the performance work

Your own response in relation to strengths, weaknesses and areas of improvement. Specific ways to improve will need to be provided, such as making schedules in order to manage time appropriately.

Page 98 Conducting a skills audit

Your own response in relation to skills, using the examples provided as a guide. Specific ways to improve will need to be included, such as regular participation in cardiovascular activities to boost stamina.

Page 99 Evaluating your ability to meet the needs of the commission brief

1. Answers should be brief/bullet points relating to issues such as whether the performance may have strayed from the stimulus/commission brief, or why it was so effective in meeting requirements of the commission brief and stimulus.
2. Answers should be more detailed, expanding on why there may have been shortcomings or explaining successes.

Page 100 Proposal: introduction

Your own proposal in response to the commission brief.

Unit 7: Employment Opportunities in the Performing Arts

These answers are in no way prescriptive and should be used for guidance only.

Page 114 The organisation

1   Answers could include:
    To make the audience think about real social issues.
    To have a collaborative approach to creating theatre.
    To produce hard-hitting, collaborative, multidisciplinary, physical theatre work.
2   Answers could include:
    To create new and exciting works.
    To raise the profile of the company in the areas in which it performs.
    To reach younger audiences through workshops in schools.
3   Answers could include highlighting words or phrases such as: original, push the boundaries, serious social issues.
4   Answers could include:
    Vision – To create new and exciting theatre.

Mission – To open the minds of young audiences to serious social issues.
Values – to present alternative points of view; to be open to new skills or approaches.

Page 115 Organisational profile: audience

1   Suggested answers could include: teenagers aged 14+; people in their early twenties who are interested in theatre; people who are interested in serious social issues.
2   Suggested answers could include:
    Audience 1: Teenagers 14+
    Reason: Because shortWIRED explores themes that teenagers can relate to, like teen pregnancy.
    Audience 2: People in their early twenties who are interested in theatre.
    Reason: Because people in their twenties might be really interested in seeing new and fresh approaches to theatre.
    Audience 3: People who are interested in serious social issues.
    Reason: Because people who are interested in serious social issues may want to learn more about them or support anything that raises awareness of the issues.
3   Suggested answers could include:
    Audience: Because the ticket money helps to subsidise the company so it can continue to do its work.
    The community: Because they are all potential audience members, and they would support the theatre company more if it addressed issues that could help to educate or enhance their community.
    Artistic director: Because their guidance would help to produce challenging work that pushes boundaries.
    The Arts Council: Because their funding can help to secure the company's future and the employment of many people in the company.
    The performers: Because their excellent skills can lead to the company having a good reputation.
4   Either regional or national. There is some reference to the 'areas' that it performs in. This is plural and suggests that shortWIRED performs in multiple locations.
5   If shortWIRED went on tour, the performers might need to be able to drive or be willing to travel.

Page 116 Organisational profile: funding

1   A charity or a community interest company.
2   Two of: grants, public donations, bursaries, public funding.
3   Suggested answers could include: take photos of workshops; produce reports on the workshops; conduct a certain number of workshops; reach a certain number of schools; produce a blog; produce a certain number of pieces during the period of funding.
4   Suggested answers could include:
    · Take photos of the workshop – ability to use a camera and edit software.
    · Produce reports on the workshops – good writing skills.
    · Conduct a certain number of workshops – ability to design workshops.
    · Reach a certain number of schools – ability to deliver workshops.
    · Produce a blog – ability to use ICT.
    · Produce a certain number of pieces during the period of funding – ability to contribute creative ideas and perform to a high standard.

Page 117 Skills required

1   Suggested answers could include: leadership skills, good planning skills, good communication skills, good subject knowledge, being personable, confidence.
2   Suggested answers could include: leadership skills, communication skills.

Page 118 Your skills

Your own response, drawn from own personal experience.

Page 119 Your qualities

Your own response, drawn from own personal experience.

Page 120 Your performance experience

Your own response, drawn from own personal experience.

Page 121 Other experience

Your own response, drawn from own personal experience.

Page 122 Workshop ideas

1 Suggested answers could include: loneliness; entitlement and how it affects us with regard to money; being superficial (consumerism); health – mental and physical.
2 Selected idea: loneliness.
3 You could be surrounded by lots of people but still feel lonely. You can explore how to show isolation through physical workshops using space and doing different body actions.

Page 123 Written response: introduction practice

Example answer:
1 My name is Dan Jordan and I am a performer based in the Midlands. I am primarily a singer, with strong acting skills.
2 I believe you are looking for performers to become members of your ground-breaking physical theatre company.
3 I have had experience in performing at several major theatres in my local area, both singing solos and as an ensemble. I have also had experience of leading singing workshops through the Young Choral Society, where I supported the conductor. My acting training included a physical theatre unit where I achieved a Merit.
4 I am interested in becoming a member of shortWIRED as I am a highly skilled performer who excels in ensemble work. I enjoy contributing to and developing ideas that are exciting and challenging to an audience.

Page 124 Written response: your skills

1 Example answer:
Skill: I am able to develop characters through research and exploration.
Experience: When performing in 'A place called …', a physical theatre piece that explored issues of homelessness, I spent an evening sleeping rough with the company so that we could fully appreciate how exposing it is and how it would affect us in the piece.
Skill: I am able to project my voice.
Experience: In 'An Inspector Calls', I performed without a microphone in a large space. I was able to maintain my volume while keeping the emotion in the voice.
2 Example answer:
I would be able to lead a workshop that either included a similar experience or else show workshop participants images from my experience to help develop their ideas in performance work. When I work with the Youth Choral Society I am given the responsibility of leading the warm-ups. I give instructions for each exercise.
In my community arts project I planned a workshop based on our devised piece called 'In the line of fire' which explored gun crime in the UK. I structured the workshop to have a warm-up, skills games and exploration tasks. I ended with small performances of what the group had worked on, and we discussed each piece.

Page 125 Written response: additional skills

1 Example answer:
I have good singing, acting and movement skills, and experience of physical theatre, which would make me suitable for this job. I have additional skills such as kick-boxing that will enable me to contribute combat movements to the creative process and I can do basic aerial work which could enhance the physical theatre approach of the company.
I can write reports to a high standard and have excellent photography skills, which will support evidencing the workshops.
2 Example answer:
I am a creative and open person and I believe that these qualities reflect your values of being open to new skills and finding new ways of saying things, and this is why I am suitable for the job.

Page 126 Written response: workshop ideas

1 Example answer:
I have had several ideas for the workshops. These include loneliness, entitlement and how it affects us moneywise, being superficial (consumerism), and physical and/or mental health.
2 Example answer:
The idea I feel most suits your organisation is loneliness because everyone can relate to it, and talking about it will mean people will realise how we are affected by it.
3 Example answer:
By the end of the workshop the participants will have created short physical theatre scenes exploring an element of loneliness.
4 Example answer:
The workshop will start with a physical and vocal warm-up. This will include walking around the room and doing some actions, building to running around the room. Once the heart rate is raised then we would look at some stretching and spine curls. Afterwards we would do some vocal exercises, starting within breathing, then humming, making sounds and looking at tongue twisters.
It will then move on to drama games. We will walk around the room solo, then as a pair, then as a small group (three or four) then as one big group. We will then reverse this and talk about how it made us feel. We will develop this by keeping some people as solos and the rest as the whole group.
It will end with separating into smaller groups to create a short scene. The groups can include any extra action or dialogue. They will perform their scenes to each other.

Page 127 Structuring your promotional portfolio

Your own response, should include your CV, headshot and body shots, video and/or audio clips and other relevant documentaiton.

Page 128 The promotional portfolio: planning

1 Example answer:

page 1	Introduction
page 2	CV
page 3	Headshot
page 4	Body shots
page 5	Performance work
page 6	Workshop leading
page 7	Audio clips
page 8	Reviews
page 9	Posters
page 10	College Training Certificates
pages 11 & 12	GCSE Certificates
page 13	Performing Arts Certificates
pages 14 & 15	References

2 Example answer:
Should you wish to see more footage of my performance work, you can access my webfolio here. I have recently participated in a workshop with Motionhouse Dance Company who produce work similar to shortWIRED and their website can be found here. Additional references are listed below.

Page 129 The promotional portfolio: your CV

Your own response, to be filled in with own details and experience.

Page 130 The promotional portfolio: audio evidence

1 Example answer:
The audio clip shows stars from *Les Miserables*. I am performing in the clip. The recording took place in a variety show at the College Theatre in 2017. In this clip I am applying strong singing techniques and you can hear my ability to emote the character of Javert from *Les Miserables*. I have good tuning and power in my voice, and this clip is an example of my vocal range.

2 Example answer:
The audio clip is 'Summertime' from *Porgy and Bess*. I am performing in the clip. The recording took place in a sound recording studio in 2017. I use projection and good tuning. In this piece you can see how rich my tone is.

Page 131 The promotional portfolio: video evidence

1 Your own selection.

2 Example answer:
The video clip is an extract from Samuel Beckett's *Waiting for Godot*. I am performing the role of Vladimir. The performance took place in the College Theatre in a workshop performance in 2017. I am performing in the video. This video clip is an example of my ability to develop character. I use facial and physical expression throughout. I am on stage left for the scene.

Page 132 The promotional portfolio: additional evidence

Example answers:
Image 2: A review of a local production of *Metamorphosis*.
In this photo is a review of my performance of Gregor in *Metamorphosis*. The journalist comments on my overall performance.
Image 3: A poster of forthcoming physical theatre production *Who Am I?*
In this poster I am the person on the top of the ladder. It is a production that I am performing in soon. I am a company member and have contributed to the development of the piece which investigated personal identity.

Page 134 The organisation

Your own proposal in response to the revision task brief.

Page 135 Organisational profile: audience

Your own proposal in response to the revision task brief.

Page 136 Organisational profile: funding

Your own proposal in response to the revision task brief.

Page 137 Skills and techniques: professional practice

Your own proposal in response to the revision task brief.

Page 138 Skills and qualities: employability

Your own proposal in response to the revision task brief.

Page 139 Workshop requirements

Your own proposal in response to the revision task brief.

Pages 140–141 Practise your written response

Your own proposal in response to the revision task brief.

Page 142 Structuring your promotional portfolio

Your own proposal in response to the revision task brief.

Page 143 The promotional portfolio: your CV

Your own proposal in response to the revision task brief.

Page 144 The promotional portfolio: evidence

Your own proposal in response to the set task brief.

Notes

Notes

Notes

Notes

Notes